TEENS'
WORKBOOK
TO
SELF
REGULATE

Empower Your Teen to Overcome Anxiety, Enhance Positive Thinking, and Develop Critical Life Skills with Proven CBT Techniques for Managing Stressful Emotions

ISABELLA FINN

3 BONUSES

Your 3 Complimentary E-books!

Scan the QR code with the camera on your phone below to get full access or go to https://www.isabellafinn.com/self-regulation-bonuses

As an EXTRA Bonus - You get the Teens Workbook to Self-Regulate in full color. Just scan with your phone below:

Join our parent support group on facebook

Questions? Feel free to email me at isabella@isabellafinn.com

Table of Contents

?

Introduction

Let me guess... your teenage years haven't been exactly what you imagined, right? You may have thought your teen years would be all about freedom and independence, but they turned out to be a bit more complicated.

Life feels like you're on an emotional rollercoaster and can't figure out how to stop it. One minute you're happy, laughing with friends and feeling on top of the world; the next, you're impulsive and bored with life. It's difficult to cope with intense emotions; your brain is overworked and you're filled with fear and self-doubt.

Perhaps you're tired of experiencing emotional distress, and it feels like you're losing control of your life—like you're on a conveyor belt with a giant grinder at the end and you have no idea how to stop the belt or get off.

You aren't alone if you can relate to any of these experiences. Many teenagers have similar experiences.

The teenage years mark the beginning of rapid growth and development.
Your body is fast transforming, your emotions are all over the place, and your mind is evolving. While these changes are a normal part of the teenage years, they can be difficult to navigate.

I was once like you, finding it difficult to get through my teenage years. I experienced sleepless nights, had "talk to the hand" moments with my parents, and desperately wanted to fit in among my peers. I wanted to be seen as a cool kid with everything figured out.

Sometimes I'd stand in front of the mirror and tear myself apart with criticisms. I second-guessed myself and had thoughts like, *I will never fit in*, *I am not good enough*, and *I will never have it figured out*. These thoughts were like a broken record, always playing in my mind.

It took some time, but I finally realized that regardless of how tough the teenage years may seem, I had the power to take control and navigate them smoothly. By mastering the skills of cognitive behavioral therapy (CBT),
I realized that my emotions don't define my life and that I could make my life easier and less stressful.

With CBT, I finally had a compass with which to navigate the unpredictable journey of my teenage years and unlock my full potential.

If you're reading this book, you're probably like my old self, who didn't kick off her teenage years smoothly. However, just like CBT techniques have changed my life and those of celebrities like Ellie Goulding and John Green, it can change yours. With CBT, I could retrain my brain, conquer negative thoughts, and regain control of my life.

Besides my personal experience using CBT during my teenage years, I'm a mom of two incredible teenagers, and I've seen it all. I've helped my kids deal with their emotional troubles and overcome intense pressure and the epic battle of self-doubt. My journey as a parent and my deep connection with teenage mental health have led me to write this book to help teenagers make their way through this important phase.

This book doesn't promise a magical cure. However, in it you'll find practical strategies to manage your emotions and overcome anxiety. You can be assured of seeing favorable results as you practice the strategies I give you.

This book will introduce you to the world of emotions—we'll discuss how to name them, understand them, and gain control over them. You'll soon be able to harness the incredible power of your emotions and use them to conquer life's challenges.

I will provide a step-by-step guide to using CBT techniques to identify negative thought patterns, challenge irrational beliefs, and develop healthier coping mechanisms.

Also, this book offers tools to handle stress effectively, guiding you in goal setting, time management, and self-care practices. It provides practical tips on initiating conversations, making friends, and gradually stepping out of your comfort zone, allowing you to thrive socially.

And since we all love a good action plan, you'll find CBT worksheets to practice mastering your emotions.

So, whether you're dealing with stress, anxiety or the everyday challenges of being a teenager, use this book as your guide to unlock your emotional superpowers, boost your personal growth, and conquer life's challenges.

Let's get started!

Chapter 1
First Things First—Your Emotions

This first chapter is where your life-changing journey begins. See it as an adventurous movie, and you're the lead character. As the lead, we will tackle your most crucial superhero abilities: your emotions.

Just as every superhero possesses superpowers that set them apart from others, emotions are like your special abilities. Understanding them is your first step toward harnessing and mastering their incredible powers.

Remember when your favorite superhero first found out they had superpowers? They struggled to master and control them. However, with time, guidance, and self-awareness they overcame their learning phase and could wield their powers for good.

That's what we're going to do with your emotions. This chapter discusses mastering your emotions by recognizing, understanding, and naming them. Let's turn your emotions into a powerful force that makes you even more awesome.

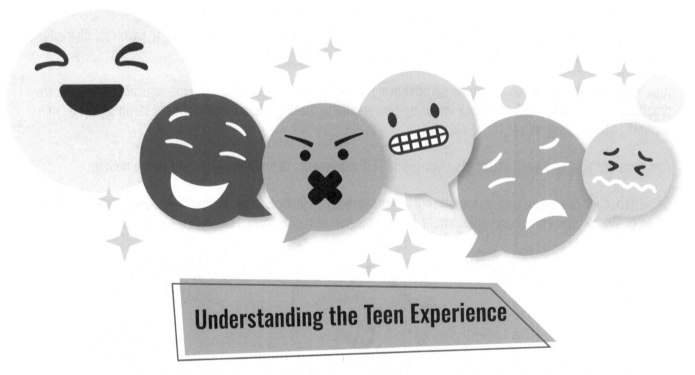

Understanding the Teen Experience

I know how crazy being a teenager can be. For me, it was like I was on a long adventure where I was both the hero and the explorer of my life—and sometimes, I felt like the villain. I can guess you've been through a similar experience, or you're approaching that point where everything seems confusing. That's because your mind and body are undergoing significant changes, and nature won't allow you to skip them. Let's discuss those changes.

Changes in Your Body

For girls, your body starts changing as early as seven years old. Some girls have their period as early as nine. For boys, your body starts changing around age nine. You might experience a growth spurt starting at age 11 and keep growing until age 21.

It's important to know that physical changes happen before emotional maturity kicks in. You might wonder, *If I look like a grown-up, why can't I act like one?* Well, physical and emotional growth doesn't always match up. It's like suddenly being in a different body, which can be exciting and confusing.

What about those mood swings? Don't panic because you're not alone; it's part of the process. Hormones play a big role in your emotional rollercoaster. One minute you're brimming with joy; the next, you feel slightly gloomy. It's like your emotions are throwing a surprise party for you.

You might have noticed that your thought process is slightly different from when you were younger, and you believe everything should be as you thought or wanted it to be. But as you enter a new stage, things keep changing, and you're confronted with new challenges—like you're leveling up in a video game.

You're starting to think more like an adult, which means you can now see the consequences of your actions, sense the complexity in situations, and contemplate abstract ideas like honesty, love, and justice. The more you talk about your ideas and listen to others, the more you think like an adult.

Teens crave independence. It was a big deal for me to make my own choices and take charge of my life during my teenage years. I saw my parents as overprotective, and I needed to challenge the rules because I felt I could do so. However, I realized that my parents wanted to keep me safe and gently expose me to the world while I developed my wings—strong enough to carry me without needing external support.

Every parent wants to be there for their kids, to guide and mentor them toward adulthood.

As your body grows, you might feel clumsy and self-conscious. Your hands and feet might grow faster than your arms and legs—imagine your feet going from size six to nine in six months! And nearly all teens deal with skin problems like acne because of hormonal changes.

You may often feel unsure of yourself and become sensitive under stress. It's common for teens to think that everyone's watching them. You worry about how you look and what you wear, and you want to be "cool" like the stars you watch on TV. Looking and dressing like your friends becomes a big deal. And yes, your friends have a huge influence on you now, so pay attention to the company you keep.

Your teen years can be split into three stages. In your early teens, your mind never stays put; it's all about mood swings. In your middle teens, you're more concerned about your appearance and are trying to figure out your limits. In the later stages, you'll have a lesser identity crisis and start thinking more like an adult, asking deep and meaningful deep questions.

Don't worry, it's all part of growing up and finding your place in the world. Don't beat yourself up because growing so quickly can make you tired and emotionally sensitive.

Tired teens are more prone to disagreements. You might have conflicts with your parents or people around you. You want to prove you can handle responsibilities and make your own decisions. However, you should take a deep breath and consider whether your parents want the best for you. Remember, they cared for you from birth, when you couldn't lift a finger, say a word, or clean yourself up. Your parents want the best for you. There's a lot of love there, even when it's hidden behind arguments.

What You Need

You need realistic expectations, a sense of self-concept, and constructive communication skills to gain control over your life. You also need a supportive environment to foster your growth. You'll do better when there are rules to guide you as you tread your path.

When I was at a crossroads in my mid-to-late teens, I felt the world was against me. However, I was lucky to have people willing to support me and explain what I could face in my teenage years. So, I embraced the rest of the ride, no matter how wild and confusing it got.

You're on a once-in-a-lifetime journey to discover who you truly are, and if you asked me, I would say it's an adventure worth every twist and turn.

You've got this!

The Emotional Rollercoaster

Although we've briefly mentioned the emotional rollercoaster with the unexpected twists and turns, let's break down some factors that can influence this wild ride leaving your feelings all over the place.

Mood swings

Have you ever gone to bed feeling like you were on cloud nine, only to wake up the next day feeling like you're wearing a hat of despair? The worst part is that you're unsure why you feel like mud. Mood swings are exactly like that and are more common in your teenage years.

Hormones

If you're looking for the culprit of this emotional rollercoaster, you can hold your hormones responsible. They're the behind-the-scenes movie directors in your body, making you appear as a superhero or a villain. They're busy transforming your body day and night and can affect your mood.

External influences

Social media, movies, and your friends greatly influence your feelings. These external influences could make you feel like being cool means you need to do something or act in a certain way, and these subtle messages are hard to ignore.

Relationship issues

Relationships with others can greatly influence an emotional rollercoaster. Imagine someone you love dearly breaking up their friendship with you—friendship might be your biggest strength one day and your biggest cause of emotional drama the next.

Self-image

In your teens, you're still figuring out who you are, where your place is, and finding order in this chaotic world. Thinking about all of this can be stressful and lead to self-doubt.

Coping skills

Riding the emotional rollercoaster might be challenging if your coping skills are poor. However, it could allow you to learn new valuable life skills, such as managing emotions, coping with stress, and navigating complex situations without breaking down.

If you have a good support system, you don't have to endure this wild rollercoaster alone. Talking to people you trust, like family members, friends, or a counselor, can improve the experience and make the journey smoother. **Don't be shy about asking for help from those you trust; they can offer support and help you navigate the ups and downs.**

Feeling a bit down is okay as you rock through an emotional rollercoaster. Tell yourself that it is all part of growing up and your journey of becoming the unique, incredible person you're meant to be.

The Science Behind Emotions

Emotions are one of the most important factors during identity formation. Your emotions largely shape how you perceive and interact with people and the world and there's some fascinating science behind them.

The limbic system, or emotional control center, is deep within your brain. It is a complicated network of components, including the amygdala, hippocampus, and hypothalamus, each of which plays a distinct role. The amygdala takes center stage, acting as your brain's emotional alert system, especially for fear and aggression. When confronted with a potentially dangerous circumstance, your body sends signals that activate your fight-or-flight reaction.

Meanwhile, the hippocampus aids in the formation of long-term memories of emotional experiences, ensuring that you do not forget those moments. What about the hypothalamus? It controls your body's emotional reaction, orchestrating changes in your pulse, perspiration, and other bodily functions based on the emotional melody your brain is playing.

Emotions don't stop at the brain; they flow through your whole body through neurotransmitters, the chemical messengers that help your brain communicate. When you feel joy, serotonin and dopamine are responsible for creating that delightful, warm feeling. On the other hand, when you feel stressed, your body will call forth adrenaline, its superhero power-up juice, boosting alertness and readiness to tackle challenges.

Hormones are a major player in all of this. When you're under pressure, the stress hormone cortisol surges, leading to feelings of anxiety. But it also keeps you on high alert, ready to face adversity head-on. And then there's oxytocin, also called the "love hormone," which activates when you're feeling affectionate or connecting with someone you care about, offering that warm, loving embrace.

While discussing the science behind emotions, we shouldn't forget to mention emotional intelligence: the art of identifying, comprehending, and directing emotions. It's like a conductor directing this emotional symphony. You can connect with others' feelings when you're emotionally intelligent, which creates wonderful harmonies in your relationships and communication.

The next time you're swept up in a whirlwind of emotions, remember that it's not just random chaos; it's the incredible arrangement of your brain and body working in harmony to help you experience all these complexities and navigate the world.

The Power of Emotions: Unleashing Your Inner Strength

Harnessing the powers of your emotions is like unlocking the hidden special abilities buried inside you. Let's explore how these powers (emotions) shape you and give you the strength to face life's challenges and the world as you grow.

Empathy

Empathy enables you to understand and share what others are feeling. When you encounter people in distress, you can feel their emotions and offer them a shoulder to lean on. Empathy is like a bridge that helps you connect with people on a deeper level and communicate better while forming meaningful relationships.

Resilience

Resilience is another of your hidden superpowers that acts like an impenetrable shield that reflects life's challenges and breaks through tough times. Resilience doesn't just help you survive—you thrive! One way to prove that you're improving is to learn from setbacks, adapting to changes and coming out stronger than before. It's like having a built-in ability for personal growth.

Positivity

Growing up, I had a friend who we nicknamed "Little Bee" because she radiated a light that attracted everyone around her and always had a smile that brightened your day. It was her superpower, and it rubbed off on us. A positive mindset is like radiating light that can brighten even the darkest days. When you find the bright side of every circumstance, you inspire yourself and everyone around you. Your positivity becomes contagious, bringing smiles and inspiration wherever you go.

Emotional Intelligence

Emotional intelligence is one of your ultimate superpowers for self-control. It is recognizing, regulating, and controlling one's emotions. With this ability, you can handle even the most difficult situations with insight. It's like having mastery over your thoughts and emotions, allowing you to make the best decisions.

Resonance

When you want to make meaningful relationships, rely on your ability to resonate and match others' frequencies. It's as if you have a magnetic force that attracts others to you. When you connect with people, you generate a sense of belonging and comprehension. You become a symbol of togetherness and collaboration, bringing out the best in people and situations.

Courage

Courage is the power that allows you to face your fears and take risks. It acts as a barrier, shielding you from self-doubt and skepticism. You can face problems, pursue your ambitions, and stand up for what you believe in when you embrace your bravery.

Adaptability

Adaptability is a special ability to thrive in a constantly changing world. You're not shocked when life throws you surprises; you overcome and thrive. You can adapt, pivot, and seize fresh opportunities. Your ability to adapt is like that of a chameleon, allowing you to blend in or stand out depending on the scenario.

The next time you feel an emotion, remember it is a special ability, not a weakness. Your emotions are your hidden powers, the inner fortitude that allows you to connect, overcome, and grow. If you embrace them, you'll discover that you're more than simply a teen; **you're a superhero** in the making.

The Power of Self-Awareness

Your self-awareness is an ability that helps you identify and understand the knowledge hidden within you. It's like having a special pair of glasses that lets you view your inner world. Understanding your characteristics, qualities, behaviors, morals, convictions, feelings, and ideas is part of this. With this skill, you can take charge and control your emotions. When you feel joy, fear, or excitement, you know it, and that knowledge gives you the ability to deal with emotions positively and healthily.

Self-awareness is not limited to emotions. It's like a special ability that helps you detect triggers in your life. When we were kids, there was this cousin we were always careful around because she had a way of pushing your buttons until you either caved in or exploded with anger. If my self-awareness ability had been as mature as it is now, those times she could set my emotions off would have been visible and I could have handled them better.**Self-awareness gives you the insight to avoid unnecessary conflicts and steer your life toward smoother paths.**

When you're at a crossroads or life throws challenges at you, self-awareness becomes a reliable compass to help you navigate them. The insight you've gained will help you make decisions with confidence. Knowing your capabilities, values, and strengths lets you make quick and sound judgments. It's like having a decision-making superpower leading you down a tailor-made path you were meant to take.

This ability also improves your relationships by allowing you to understand the impact of your words and actions on other people. With this knowledge, you can settle problems, establish stronger connections, and communicate more effectively. It's like a magic technique for creating peaceful relationships.

Being self-aware helps raise your self-esteem. You will see how confident you are when you truly know yourself. You'll appreciate your individuality and have faith in your skills. It's like having a boost of self-worth that gives you the bravery to face obstacles head-on.

It doesn't end there. **This ability also helps you find better ways to combat stress.** You can achieve effective stress management by identifying and responding to your stressors. It's like having a shield to protect you from the stress storm.

One of the most unique self-awareness abilities lies in **self-improvement and personal growth.** Understanding and acknowledging your weaknesses will help you improve, track progress, and evolve. This ability is like a compass pointing you toward the best version of yourself.

Ultimately, self-awareness is the golden key to happiness and fulfillment.

Exercise: The Mood Diary

Navigating adolescence can be quite the emotional rollercoaster. Some days you may feel low on energy or like you're in the lowest valley, while other days you're filled with energy and on top of the world. But worry not, because you can take charge of your emotions, and the tool for that is the mood diary, a reliable companion on your journey.

Step 1: Daily Check-In (2 Minutes)

Take a moment to note how you're feeling at a particular time daily. Measure and write how you feel, using a scale from 1 (low) to 5 (high). This is your emotional weather report.

Step 2: Identify Patterns (2 Minutes)

After a week of doing step 1, look back. Do you notice any trends? Are there certain activities or times of day that affect your mood? Jot down your observations.

Step 3: Decode Emotional Storms (3 Minutes)

When you're faced with a challenging emotion, write it down. Describe in detail what happened, how you felt, and what the trigger might have been. This detail will help you understand and control your emotions.

Step 4: Celebrate the Sunny Days (1 Minute)

Always remember to record moments of joy and positivity. Even a brief note about why you felt happy or what made you feel good can go a long way in brightening your day.

Step 5: Share and Communicate (2 Minutes)

You can share your mood diary with someone you trust and are comfortable with. It's a conversation starter, making it easier for them to support you.

Step 6: Track Your Progress (2 Minutes)

Examine your mood diary periodically. See how much you've grown and progressed on your journey, and don't forget to celebrate your achievements. Use this as your growth map.

Step 7: Empower Yourself (1 Minute)

Remember that having a mood diary empowers you to take charge of your emotional journey. You now have the tools to manage the highs and lows of life, recognize your triggers, and steer toward the emotional landscapes you want.

This activity is like a daily adventure inside your emotional realm.

So have fun!

Exercise: Mindfulness for Emotional Regulation

Mindfulness is one of the best tools for emotional regulation. It's like having a remote control with a button that helps you stay calm and control your emotions. This exercise will help you practice mindfulness and harness its power.

Presence

Being present means your thoughts and actions are fully in the present moment. Visualize your feelings and thoughts as moving clouds floating in the sky, and observe them objectively without judgment, emotions, or extra thoughts. Practicing this mindfulness technique is like creating a pause button for your emotions.

Four-count deep breathing

Stay calm and take a deep and slow breath when your emotions are rocking out of your control. Inhale slowly for a count of four, hold your breath for another count of four, and exhale for a final count of four. This breathing exercise is like a dam for your flooding emotions.

Body scan

Sit comfortably, close your eyes, and relax your body. Then, mentally scan your entire body. Take note of all the areas where you feel tight or uncomfortable. Breathe deeply into those spots, allowing the tension to melt away. This technique has a healing power on your emotional condition and gives you better control of your mental state.

Grounding exercise

Use your mind to tether yourself to something and ground yourself in the present moment. Focus on your inner world and name five things you sense. This exercise is like an anchor that keeps you steady in your emotional storm.

Acceptance

Practicing self-compassion helps you embrace your emotions without being judgmental. Emotional storms are like crashing ocean waves; they come and go. Accepting yourself provides you with a shield against self-criticism.

Letting go of control

Your emotions are calmer when you let go of fears, doubts, and worries weighing on your mind. Sometimes life throws challenges our way. Mindfulness helps you accept the unexpected and adapt with elegance. It's like flexible armor wrapped around you, protecting you against surprises.

Staying curious

Always stay curious about your emotions. This way, you can periodically ask yourself why you feel a certain way. These queries are like lanterns that light up the darkness of confusion.

Gratitude practice

End your day by identifying three things you're grateful for. Gratitude is like a magical tool that shifts your focus from negativity to positivity.

Patience

Recall that mindfulness is a skill, and like any other skill, it takes time to perfect. So, go easy on yourself. This patience will help guide you through the storm like a soft wind.

Consistency

Make mindfulness one of your everyday habits. The secret to unlocking a higher level is consistency. It's like fueling your emotional abilities.

Mindfulness allows you to control your emotions, maintain composure in the face of difficulty, and gracefully handle unexpected challenges. Accept this power, then see how it changes your emotional terrain into resilience and serenity.

Exercise: CBT Worksheet for Emotional Mastery

Follow the instructions in this worksheet and use your results to understand, manage, and regulate your emotions.

This worksheet is a daily mood tracker designed to help you monitor and understand your daily moods and emotions. You can also see it as your emotional compass guiding your day.

☐ **Date and day of the week:**
Fill in the date and the day of the week on the day you're tracking.

☐ **Mood/emotion:**
Write down the mood or emotion you're experiencing that day.

☐ **Intensity (1–10):**
On a scale from 1 to 10, rate the intensity of this emotion, where 1 is very low and 10 is very high.

☐ **Activities:**
Take note of any significant activities or events that may have influenced or triggered your mood. For example, you can include talking with someone, work- or school-related activities, parties, social interactions, exercise, or anything you consider an activity.

☐ **Notes:**
Use this space to add notes or thoughts concerning your mood or day. Feel free to include details about what went well, what could have been better, what went sideways, or any other observations.

Your turn now! Fill out this worksheet.

Daily Mood Tracker	Answers
Date:	
Day of the Week:	
Mood/Emotion:	
Intensity (1-10):	
Activities:	
Notes:	

Tracking your daily moods can provide valuable insights into your emotional patterns and ways to improve them. You can use this tool as your guide to navigating your daily emotional landscape.

Finally, although your emotions can come crashing down like a tidal wave, they're not your enemies—instead, you should view them as your allies. They provide depth and meaning to your life. As you grow and gain more experience, you'll improve your emotional intelligence and self-awareness. So, get ready to unleash your inner strength as we continue on an exciting journey of self-discovery and emotional mastery.

Chapter 2
Taming Anxiety Monsters

Everyone experiences anxiety; no one is immune. When you're under pressure, faced with uncertainty, or in a new and challenging situation, it's normal to feel anxious. These days, anxiety feels like a constant state for many people.

Though you may be able to hide the signs of anxiety, such as a faster heartbeat and a pit in your stomach, it's been proven that constantly being in a state of anxiety can be detrimental to one's physical and mental health.

Regardless of what makes you anxious, anxiety can be uncomfortable. It evokes worrying thoughts and strong physiological responses. Unfortunately, the physical responses to anxiety tend to increase the intensity of the emotion. Thus, you find yourself in a vicious cycle that is incredibly difficult to break.

How you respond to distressing emotions such as anxiety can make a significant difference in the intensity and duration of the accompanying feelings. In other words, responding to anxious feelings in an unhealthy way can make the feelings stronger and last longer.

You may be making certain mistakes that are amplifying your anxiety and making the monsters roar louder. But the good news is that **you can transform the emotion into a superpower rather than a limitation through specific CBT strategies, such as identifying triggers and challenging and reframing the negative thoughts fueling anxiety.** With this, you can learn to respond to anxious feelings healthily.

In this chapter, we'll explore the various types of anxiety disorders, the causes of anxiety, and how to identify triggers. Most importantly, we'll look at CBT techniques for coping with anxiety.

Understanding Anxiety: Friend or Foe?

Millions of people consider anxiety a negative emotional state. After all, it makes us so uncomfortable that we wish it didn't exist. When anxious, your stomach tightens, your heart races, and your palms soak with sweat. You may avoid hanging out with friends or partaking in activities that others appear to enjoy easily. You may worry about things that haven't happened, disrupting your focus and sleep. So, why wouldn't you consider anxiety a foe?

The best way to think of anxiety is as both friend and foe—or neither. Anxiety, as an emotion, is woven into our very nature to protect us from threat or danger. It's been there from the beginning of existence and evolved with us as we evolved.

Anxiety doesn't feel like much of a friend when it attacks out of the blue in the form of a panic attack. But the problem is that we often fail to notice the signs as they creep up on us, and then it hits!

Let's examine anxiety more closely.

As I said, this emotion is wired into everyone. It tells us when something is wrong and prepares us to fight or flee. Without anxiety, evolution wouldn't have been possible since early humans wouldn't have survived the many threats and dangers they faced.

Therefore, on some level, **anxiety is a friend because it is the body's natural alarm system. It has a purpose: to inform you when something has to change**. To prepare you for a threat, anxiety quickens your breathing, tightens your chest, and narrows your vision. It also pumps blood to your muscles so that you can fight or flee for your survival.

Like all emotions, **anxiety exists on a spectrum**; it can range from mild to severe. In some people, anxiety occurs acutely, whereas it's chronic in others. Sometimes it's necessary and helpful. For instance, being anxious about a meeting can motivate you to leave your home on time and avoid the traffic.

However, too much anxiety can impair your ability to focus and perform at your best. It can even make you withdraw and avoid certain situations. Of course, you don't want that to happen. That's why it helps to learn how to tame anxiety and ensure it doesn't become a regular emotional state.

There are plenty of ways to change how you respond to anxiety, but you'll need practice. First, you must learn to identify what triggers anxious feelings and label how you feel. But before we discuss how to do that, let's explore the different types of anxiety disorders. That way, you'll know the specific type of anxiety you struggle with and how best to manage it.

Types of Anxiety Disorders

Anxiety is the body's response to stress, and experiencing it in some situations can be beneficial. It alerts you to danger, helps you to pay attention, and activates the "fight or flight" mode. However, anxiety disorders are not the same as regular feelings of anxiousness or nervousness.

Unlike regular anxious feelings, anxiety disorders are characterized by excessive fear or worry. They are the most common mental health problems.

Occasional anxiety is an inevitable part of life. It's okay to feel anxious from time to time. But when you have an anxiety disorder, you have intense, persistent, and excessive feelings of fear and worry regarding everyday situations.

Sometimes, anxiety disorders are marked by regular episodes of sudden feelings of intense fear or terror that peak within a few minutes. These are called panic attacks. Excessive worry and panic disrupt a person's daily routine, are hard to manage, and are disproportionate to the perceived threat. They tend to last longer than normal.

These feelings can cause you to avoid people, places, or situations. Symptoms of anxiety disorders typically begin in childhood or adolescence and continue into adulthood.

Common types of anxiety disorders include:

Generalized anxiety disorder

Generalized anxiety disorder (GAD) is marked by excessive and persistent worry that disrupts an individual's day-to-day life. The worry from GAD is often accompanied by physical symptoms including restlessness, fatigue, difficulty focusing, tense muscles, and sleep problems. People with GAD tend to worry about everyday things like family responsibilities, health, appointments, chores, etc.

This anxiety disorder can impair different areas of your life. It can affect your ability to maintain employment, leave the house, or travel as well as your energy, sleep, and focus.

Social anxiety disorder (social phobia)

Everyone feels varying degrees of anxiety about social or performance situations. Social anxiety disorder, also called social phobia, is when you have an excessive fear or dread of situations that require social interaction. It can occur before, during, or after a social event.

Individuals with social anxiety disorder experience severe discomfort and anxiety about being humiliated, embarrassed, or ridiculed in social situations. They often worry that they'll do something embarrassing in public. A person with this disorder will either endure great anxiety during social interactions or try to avoid them altogether.

Examples include an intense fear of eating or drinking in public, meeting new people, and public speaking. The anxiety creates problems with everyday functioning and persists for at least half a year.

Specific phobia

A specific phobia is a persistent and irrational fear of certain objects, activities, or situations that are generally not risky or harmful. An individual with a specific phobia knows their fear is irrational, but they can't manage it. The fear triggers such intense distress that the person might take extreme actions to avoid the source. Specific phobias include fear of heights, public speaking, and spiders.

Panic disorder

Panic disorder is characterized by recurrent anxiety attacks involving a combination of psychological and physiological symptoms. During a panic attack, you may experience many of these symptoms simultaneously:

- Rapid heart rate
- Trembling
- Shortness of breath or a feeling of being smothered
- Sweating
- Chest pain
- Tingling or numbness
- Feeling of being choked
- Dizziness or light-headedness
- Fear of dying

Due to the severity of the symptoms, someone having a panic attack may think it's a heart attack or other life-threatening illness. Sometimes panic attacks occur out of the blue; other times they occur as a response to a feared situation.

As previously mentioned, the occasional experience of anxiety is normal. However, when it becomes constant and overwhelming, that's an anxiety disorder. You might avoid school, work, get-togethers, and social situations due to crippling fear or worry caused by an anxiety disorder.

In general, the dominant symptom of all anxiety disorders is irrational and excessive fear or worry. Still, they have other common symptoms. All types of anxiety disorders can make it difficult to breathe, stay still, focus, and sleep. Your symptoms will be determined by the specific anxiety disorder you have.

Now, let's talk about the causes of anxiety and anxiety disorders.

Exploring the Causes

Everyone experiences anxiety differently, so it can be hard to identify the exact cause of your anxiety. There may be several factors at play. Still, knowing the root of your anxiety is key to finding effective ways to tame it in the long term.

Anxiety symptoms often have a specific cause, which may be beyond your awareness. Beneath the racing heart, sweaty palms, and bottomless pit in your stomach is an underlying reason for what you're feeling.

Sometimes, the cause of anxiety is specific to a person and their circumstances. For instance, you may feel anxious due to an upcoming test at school. If you have social anxiety, it may be due to an inner belief that you aren't good enough.

Often, when we experience anxiety symptoms, we fixate on the physical sensations and symptoms. This is normal since the signs are usually too loud to ignore. But as you focus on easing the nervousness, you may ignore whatever is happening beneath the surface.

Using CBT-based anxiety coping strategies without identifying the root of your fear or worry is akin to slapping a band-aid on an injury—it offers a quick fix but doesn't address the problem. Consequently, you could end up leaving the root problem unresolved.

Exploring the cause of your anxiety may comprise two vital steps:

- Identifying what you're afraid of
- Recognizing why you're afraid of it

Completing both steps can empower you and help you make progress in your journey toward taming your anxiety monsters.

So, how do you explore the cause of your anxiety?

First, manage the current symptoms to nurture a clear mind for self-reflection and introspection. Place one hand on your belly and the other on your chest to do this. Then, breathe in deeply and exhale. Notice how your chest and belly expand when you inhale and exhale. Do this a few times and then grab a notebook to explore the underlying cause of your anxiety, following these steps:

Keep an open and kind mindset.

Treating yourself as you would a close friend is important as you begin this process. Explore with curiosity, compassion, and patience. Take this step to understand yourself more. Be gentle with yourself and proceed with kindness.

Get familiar with your anxiety.

For effective self-exploration, you need an understanding of how your anxiety functions. In your notebook, write down when you typically experience anxiety, where it occurs, what happens physically and psychologically, and how long the symptoms last.

Write down your fears.

Articulating what you're really afraid of gives you a real monster to tame rather than the mere idea of monsters. So, create a list of things that make you anxious, starting each with "*I am scared of...*" or "*I'm worried about...*" Write everything that comes to mind about what makes you afraid.

Identify a pattern.

Finding patterns and connecting the dots can make recognizing the root of your anxiety easier. To see if there's a pattern, answer the following questions:

- ☐ How long has it been since I didn't feel as I do now?
- ☐ Has anything changed in my life over the last three to six months or years? If yes, what?
- ☐ Have I felt this way during other times, past or present, in different situations?
- ☐ If yes, what were these moments? Is there a recurring theme between the situations?

Reflect on your home life.

Your anxiety may be connected to your home life or childhood. This isn't about blaming your parents or yourself. Instead, it's about acknowledging that your family might have hurt you with their words or actions. So, explore the following questions, focusing on the details of your memories and the feelings that surface:

- ☐ What were my upbringing and relationships with my family like?
- ☐ Did I feel invalidated, dismissed, ridiculed, punished, or scared at any time in my childhood?
- ☐ Was I ever made to feel like I wasn't good enough or like a burden?
- ☐ Was I ever made to feel like it wasn't okay to express my feelings and needs?

Focus on your habits.

Sometimes, our habits are the underlying cause of anxiety. Not sleeping enough can trigger daytime anxiety. Poor food choices such as eating fast food can also lead to anxiety. To explore whether your habits are the root, answer these questions:

- ☐ Has the frequency, duration, or intensity of my anxiety increased recently?
- ☐ How do I sleep? Do I get enough sleep daily?
- ☐ Have I been drinking enough water?
- ☐ Have I changed any habits or picked up new ones lately?

When suffering from an anxiety disorder, it's normal to want the symptoms to go away. However, anxiety management techniques without exploring the root of the problem make it difficult to find meaningful long-term solutions.

Recurring anxiety is usually a sign of an unresolved problem. So, pinpoint what you're scared of and explore the reason to help yourself.

Recognizing Anxiety Triggers

What triggers anxiety for you will depend on the specific type of anxiety disorder you have and the stressors in your life. Triggers may include life events, unhealthy habits, or things that are out of your control. They can cause you to experience common anxiety symptoms such as excessive worry, tension, restlessness, racing thoughts, difficulty concentrating, and irritability.

If left unchecked, anxiety triggers can lead to panic attacks and other severe mental health conditions. Of course, to manage them, you have to know what they are first. So, here's how to recognize your anxiety triggers:

Keep a journal.

Writing down your feelings in a journal is a great way to track them and identify patterns that you may not otherwise notice. It's also helpful for analyzing situations that make you afraid or anxious. So, start recording moments when you have anxiety attacks and what led up to them.

Identify stressors.

Are there certain things you're constantly thinking about even when you don't feel particularly anxious? Relationship changes, job loss, and moving are some major stressors that can worsen anxiety symptoms and make them last longer.

Think about past experiences.

Previous negative experiences can act as anxiety triggers. Reflect on any past experience that might still influence your thoughts and feelings today.

Common anxiety triggers include:

- Health problems
- Relationship problems
- Stress
- Conflict at home, work, or school
- Social events
- Caffeine
- Medication
- Finances
- Public speaking
- Sleep problems
- Major changes in routine

Recognizing your anxiety trigger may take significant time and effort, but it's necessary for mastering the proper coping skills needed to manage your anxiety. Once you know your triggers, it's easier to cope with them.

Exercise: Challenging Anxious Thoughts with CBT

Anxiety can take a harmless thought and escalate it within minutes, leading to a catastrophe, which eventually makes the thought a reality.

For example, let's say you sent a text to your boyfriend or girlfriend in the morning, asking to meet up later tonight. It's 2 p.m. and they still haven't replied. You might think, *Oh, they probably didn't see my text.* Or you might think, *They no longer like me! They want to break up, and that's why they're ignoring my text!*

It's easy to react to anxious thoughts as though they are real. You have both physical and emotional reactions. Cognitive behavioral therapy (CBT) is highly effective for treating anxiety disorders because it focuses primarily on challenging the negative thoughts or beliefs that fuel anxiety. CBT techniques teach you to reframe anxious thoughts that may be fueling your disorder. By doing this, you can relieve distress and tame your anxiety.

Anxiety has a purpose: It alerts you to a problem and forces you to focus on it so that you can solve the problem. But when it grows out of control, anxiety does the opposite of this—it impairs your problem-solving ability. When this occurs, anxious thoughts (irrational or negative thoughts) typically play a part.

The Challenging Anxious Thoughts exercise teaches you to recognize and replace your anxious thoughts with more rational ones. With regular practice, this will become a natural way of managing anxiety.

Here's the worksheet for challenging your anxious thoughts.

Describe a situation that makes you feel anxious:

Example: "*speaking in front of more than two people*" or "*going on a date*"

Anxiety fuels irrational thinking by making you overestimate the possibility of something negative happening and exaggerate the potential consequences to be much worse than they are. Sometimes, all you need to alleviate anxious thoughts is to challenge them with facts.

Imagine you're in the anxiety-triggering situation from above. Write down the...

Worst possible outcome:

Best possible outcome:

Likely outcome:

Now, imagine if the worst possible outcome happens. Would it still affect your life...

A week from now:

A month from now:

A year from now:

Anxious thoughts force you to fixate on the worst possible outcomes, even when the odds of them coming true are ridiculously low. For example, suppose you're giving a speech in front of your classmates. In that case, you might think, *I won't remember anything I memorized, and I'll be embarrassed, and everybody in school will make fun of me forever.*

Next, using your "worst outcome" and "likely outcome" written above, write down your...

Anxious (irrational) thought:

Rational thought:

Finally, replace the anxious thought with the rational thought you devise. Returning to the earlier example of a boyfriend or girlfriend not replying to your text in hours, you might reframe your anxious thoughts: *They're probably busy and haven't had time to check their phone. They'll contact me as soon as they see the message.*

Challenging and reframing anxious thoughts in the moment can instantly relieve anxiety symptoms.

Cognitive behavioral therapy operates on the idea that our thoughts dictate how we feel, which, in turn, determines how we act. **Thought influences emotion and behavior.** And by changing how you think and reframing your experiences, you can change how you feel. Shifting perception by challenging and reframing your thoughts allows you to gain control and manage your emotional reactions more effectively.

To do this, you have to capture anxious and irrational thoughts. This is possible through the *Thought Record* technique, a key part of CBT. In fact, it's been called the "Swiss Army Knife of CBT."

This exercise aims to teach you about the connection between your thoughts, feelings, and behaviors while serving as a tool for recording your experiences. The thought record is the best place to begin if you want to challenge your anxious thoughts.

Writing down your thoughts in a structured way is an excellent method for capturing dysfunctional thinking patterns. The more you record your thoughts, the greater your awareness of negative or irrational thinking.

The best time to have a thought record session is shortly after you notice a change in your feelings. When you notice a mood shift, take a few minutes to observe what you're thinking at that moment, and then write it down in the "Automatic Thoughts" column. Then, write down what you did when the mood change occurred in the "Situation" column. After this, complete the rest of the rows accordingly.

Here's a template for recording your thoughts.

Situation	Automatic Thoughts	Emotions	Alternative Thoughts
(What were you doing?) Example: I was preparing for my school presentation.	*(What thoughts popped into your head at that moment?)* Example: I will forget everything I memorized and embarrass myself, and my classmates will make fun of me forever.	*(How did you feel at the time? How intense was the emotion?)* Example: I felt crippling fear and anxiety that was so intense that I started to sweat and my heart raced.	*(Is there any evidence to support the automatic thought? Could there be a different explanation?)* Example: There's no way I'll forget everything. I am studying hard, after all. And even if that happens, everyone will forget and move on after a few days.

When completing a thought record, consider the following:

- ☐ Is there any evidence to support your thought?
- ☐ What is the evidence for and against the thought?
- ☐ Are there alternative explanations or perspectives?
- ☐ What is the worst possible outcome, and how would you cope if that happened?
- ☐ What is the best possible outcome?
- ☐ What is the most realistic outcome?
- ☐ What is the potential result of giving in to your anxious thoughts?

Then, answer these questions:

- ☐ What would happen if you changed your thinking?
- ☐ What would you tell a close friend in a similar situation?
- ☐ What should you do next?

You'll find thought records incredibly useful for organizing your thoughts and choosing your responses.

Exercise: CBT Worksheet for Anxiety

Identifying triggers

Write down thoughts, events, or situations that make you feel anxious. Rate the intensity of the anxious feelings triggered by each thought on a scale of 1 to 10.

Trigger	Rating
Public speaking	8
Crowds	7
Financial problems	9
Going on a date	10
Health concerns	8

Recognizing physical symptoms

List physical symptoms you experience when anxious. Rate how intense each symptom is on a scale of 1 to 10.

Symptom	Rating
Racing heart	9
Sweating	8
Trembling	7
Shallow breathing	6

Challenging anxious thoughts

Write down recurring anxious thoughts that accompany your triggers.

I'll embarrass myself during my presentation.

Presenting evidence for and against

Write down past experiences that can act as evidence to support and contradict your thoughts.

Supporting: I have previously experienced nervousness during another presentation.

Contradicting: My classmates and teacher provided positive feedback the last time I did a presentation. Only one person tried to make me feel bad.

Reframing the anxious thought

Come up with a more realistic or rational thought to counteract the anxious one.

> I have adequately prepared and will perform well during the presentation.

>

>

>

>

Trying a healthy coping strategy

Use this "4-7-8" deep breathing exercise as a coping strategy for managing your anxiety.

The 4-7-8 breathing exercise involves inhaling to a count of 4, holding your breath to a count of 7, and exhaling to a count of 8. It is a common form of rhythmic breath regulation used in yoga that can reduce anxiety and induce relaxation.

Here's how to do the exercise:

- ☐ Empty your lungs of air.
- ☐ Inhale quietly through the nose as you count to 4.
- ☐ Hold your breath as you count to 7.
- ☐ Breathe out through the mouth, purse your lips, and make a "whoosh" sound as you count to 8.
- ☐ Repeat the first four steps up to five times.

You may feel lightheaded after the first few sessions of a deep breathing exercise, so only practice when lying down or sitting to ensure you don't get dizzy.

In the next chapter, we'll discuss managing stress effectively with various coping techniques such as goal setting and time management.

Chapter 3
Mastering Stress Management

It's not news that stepping into the teenage phase of life comes with some stress. But I have some pleasant information for you in this chapter: We'll discuss stress management and how it can impact your life.

Dealing with stress might not be as easy as you thought when you were younger. The stressors in the younger stage of your life are not comparable to those in adolescence. To deal with stress, you need to learn some vital life skills. The good news is that these skills are relevant for all life stages, not just the teenage phase.

Let's start with understanding the differences between stress and eustress.

Stress vs Eustress: Understanding the Difference

Stress and eustress may seem alike, but they are not as similar as you may think. Stress is the more commonly used term, which happens when you're anxious, overwhelmed, or sense a threat. Let's say you're working on a group assignment and suddenly a member of the group makes a severe mistake that requires you to start from the beginning. The feeling of worry and anxiety that follows this is stress, and most times, it does not happen in isolation—it comes with a lot of negative thoughts and sometimes, aggression.

Eustress is also stress, but has some positives. You don't feel anxious but curious. Instead of feeling wrong about what's happening, you feel motivated to take on the challenge, and there's a positive energy that comes with it that prevents negative consequences.

So why does it matter?

How you see or respond to these types of stress determines your experience. If you view the stress from a negative perspective, then it will have a significant effect on your physical and mental health, and this can lead to headaches, insomnia, and anxiety. You don't want to go through any of those, which brings us to turning your stress into eustress.

Eustress, unlike stress, can be beneficial to you. It serves as a trigger for you to achieve your goals, step out of your comfort zone to overcome challenges, and most importantly, grow. You know that scolding you get from your dad just to set you on track? That's how eustress works.

Ultimately, stress and eustress may sound similar, but it's all about how we perceive and handle them. Do you know your stress triggers? They are those events or situations that activate stress.

I don't know about you, but my greatest stress trigger is meeting deadlines. Imagine having five assignments to turn in at the same time. It automatically makes me stressed, and every tick of the clock builds tension. Stress triggers can come in many forms: school, chores, relationships. Don't overreact when you experience one. Identify it and use the strategies we'll discuss in this chapter to manage it.

The Impact of Stress

Stress will mess with your physical, mental, and emotional well-being. One moment everything is going fine, and the next, you begin to feel anxious and you're completely stressed. That's a glimpse of what stress can do to you.

Have you ever noticed that there are specific reactions you feel inside of you when you feel stressed? Those are physical signs of stress. Headaches, muscle tension, stomach aches, insomnia, and irritability can all be caused by stress.

Another area of your life stress affects is your relationships. When you feel stressed, you become moody, sad, anxious, and irritable, which can make you aggressive or want to be alone.

I'm sure you have heard of depression. Do you know that stress can also lead to depression? If you undergo too much stress, it takes a toll on your emotions, making you sad and angry. If you do not handle stress well, it gradually grows into depression. So, it's important to note these impacts and be proactive when you notice them.

Managing Stress

I don't think one can exist without going through some form of stress. Knowing that stress will always come, it's important we discuss ways to manage it and avoid the negative consequences that come with it.

Harness Stress for Growth

Stress might be one of the worst feelings ever, but it's not all negative, as mentioned earlier. Sometimes, stress can push you out of your comfort zone and help you achieve big things. It could motivate you to see the end of what's stressing you out, and if you have this mentality, you will view stress as a tool to improve. Instead of trying to escape stress, why not embrace it, turn it into eustress, and get the best out of it?

You might be asking yourself, *How can stress be a good thing?* When you face situations that stress you, your emotional gear is high, and your body releases hormones like adrenaline. This increases your alertness and gives you a higher probability of performing better than usual.

Another positive side of stressful situations is that they can teach you things about yourself. When stress pushes you to your limit, you discover your strengths and weaknesses. Once you can breeze through, you learn to adapt and solve your problems, leading to positive growth. Do you now agree that stress can have some positive sides?

The Power of Goal Setting

Trust me, setting goals for yourself is a game-changer in stress management. When you outline goals for yourself, you're giving yourself a guide to work with and things to focus on. This helps you reduce stress because your mind is set on the goals you have set for yourself.

Setting goals makes you feel in control of your life. When stress comes, the fact that you already have a goal in sight calms you, and when you finally reach the goal, you're fulfilled, and your self-confidence is boosted. Less stress, more control over your life, and a great confidence boost—a fantastic situation if you ask me. Pick up that journal and set those goals now.

Remember that it isn't just about the big and long-term goals. You can also set small and short-term goals. The smaller ones can even make the bigger ones more achievable.

Time Management

When you have proper time management, you're indirectly reducing your stress levels—killing two birds with one stone. To avoid that overwhelming feeling of having too much to do at once, you need to have a clear plan and prioritize your tasks. Trust me, I've been there, and it's not something you want to experience. Break down the goals you've set into very small ones so you can manage your time and tackle these goals one by one. The feeling of accomplishment afterward is unexplainable unless experienced.

If you feel like you're too engaged with activities and can't get enough time for yourself, then you need time management. When you're organized with your time, you can leave some for yourself to do the things you love, which is essential for your well-being.

Overcome Procrastination

Sometimes we get the urge to put things off until later and continue with life. This is called procrastination, and it's a bad habit that largely contributes to stress. Procrastinating will never make a task disappear. It only worsens matters because you will still face it later and may be unable to do it to the best of your ability. Why not face your tasks right away and tick them off your list? You lift a huge burden off your head by not procrastinating.

However, this habit is not easy to overcome. You need intentionality, effort, and discipline. To make it easier, break your large tasks into smaller ones so they don't feel overwhelming. Every mini-task accomplished is a step closer to achieving the big ones.

Engage in Self-Care

When you feel extremely stressed, the first approach to tackle it is to take good care of yourself. You don't even need to do too much. Just know what self-care practices work for you and stick to them.

There's no standard way to engage in self-care, but there are many ways to achieve it. I love to listen to good jazz music, eat some homemade food, and relax. For some people, it's visiting a spa, hanging out with friends, or playing their favorite sport. What matters is to know what works for you. You're not being selfish by indulging in self-care; you're simply putting yourself in a good state to be able to face life's challenges.

Stress can stretch you to your limits, and you cannot afford not to practice self-care. It's a very effective strategy to combat stress. Eat well, exercise, get enough sleep, and have some fun. Do all of this and see how much lower your stress levels are.

Building Resilience: Stress as a Stepping Stone

Resilience is the ability to bounce back from difficulties, challenges, or setbacks. You're resilient when you can adapt to change or positively overcome challenges. But do you know that stress can be a stepping stone to building resilience? It's like learning a challenging musical piece; it makes it easier to learn other tough ones you encounter.

How can you build resilience in the face of stress?

First, be positive. In every situation, try to look at the positive side and not the negative. Seek solutions rather than capitalizing on the problems. This will help you reframe your negative thoughts into positive ones and progress on your resilience journey.

Next, face your fears. The more you face the things that stress you, the better coping mechanisms you'll learn to deal with them. Be consistent with this, and you'll see yourself becoming resilient.

Ensure you build solid and meaningful relationships with people around you because these are the people who will provide you with the emotional support and guidance you need.

Exercise: Encouraging Mindfulness

Deep Breathing

I'll begin with the most popular mindfulness practice: deep breathing. This exercise is one of the easiest to do.

- Relax in a comfortable position.
- Breathe in through your nose until your stomach is filled up.
- Hold it in for a few seconds.
- Gradually let out the air through your mouth.

Trust me, the bliss that comes after this exercise is unmatched. It is one of my go-to exercises whenever I am anxious, and it works like magic.

Candle Gazing

Another mindfulness exercise you can try is the *candle gazing exercise.* All you need is a candle and a tranquil space.

- Light the candle.
- Quietly gaze at the flames and settle your mind.
- Avoid distractions and put your entire focus on the flames as they gradually escape into the air.

This exercise helps you relax and concentrate. Give it a try—you won't be disappointed.

Gratitude List

This exercise keeps you glued to the things you're thankful for and shifts your focus away from the things that are not working. It's pretty simple and best done in the mornings before you start your daily activities.

- Get a pen and a piece of paper or open the notes app in your phone.
- Write 10 to 20 things you're grateful for and then read through them. You'll notice that after reading through, you're filled with positive vibes and ready to start your day on a good note.

When you focus on the good things in your life, you see life from a positive perspective and begin to appreciate the little things you once overlooked. Start counting your blessings and watch the magic happen.

Exercise: SMART Goals

Setting your goals the **SMART** way will help you set realistic and achievable ones. **SMART** stands for Specific, Measurable, Achievable, Relevant, and Time-bound.

Let me break down each letter:

S - Specific:
Be clear and detailed about your goal.

M - Measurable:
Set goals that allow you to monitor your progress.

A - Achievable:
Set goals that are realistic and within your means.

R - Relevant:
Ensure your goals align with your objectives and that you're working towards the things that matter.

T - Time-Bound:
Set timeframes for your goals. This will keep you focused and motivated. How good does it feel to meet a deadline? Do the same for your goals and get that satisfactory feeling.

Now, fill out this **SMART** worksheet.

SMART Goal	
SPECIFIC: *What goals do I want to achieve?*	
MEASURABLE: *What are the signs that I've started achieving my goals?*	
ACHIEVABLE: *What are the things I need to do to achieve these goals?*	
RELEVANT: *What do I stand to gain after achieving these goals?*	
TIME-BOUND: *How long will I give myself to achieve these goals?*	

After completing this, write an action plan summarizing everything you've written in the worksheet and stick to it.

Exercise: Stressors and Coping Strategies

This goal of this exercise is to identify the stressors in your life and brainstorm coping strategies you can use to manage them.

Here is a worksheet that has been filled out to give you some ideas about potential stressors and effective coping strategies. Study it.

Stressor	Coping Strategies
Academic pressure	• List tasks and set goals. • Break tasks into small, manageable steps. • Ask for help. • Manage my time.
Social conflicts	• Communicate clearly with the people involved. • Confide in and seek support from trusted adults. • Listen actively without distractions.
Family dynamics	• Talk to the family member involved about the issues. • Establish boundaries and list expectations. • Be empathic and understanding.
Extracurricular activities	• Evaluate commitments and eliminate less important ones. • Create time for self-care and relaxation. • Delegate tasks if possible.

Your turn!

Stressor	Coping Strategies

After filling out the table, reflect on the coping strategies that resonate most with you. Consider incorporating them into your daily life to help you manage stress.

Exercise: Stress-Busting Playlist

Music is an effective tool for improving your mood and reducing stress. This exercise is all about creating a stress-busting playlist. Let's get started!

Write down the titles of the songs you love listening to when you feel under pressure or stressed.

Write down the artist of each song.

For each song you've written, write down why you like it. Is it the melody, lyrics, rhythm, or a memory associated with it?

- _____
- _____
- _____
- _____
- _____
- _____

When do you like listening to each song? When you feel overwhelmed, before bedtime, during a study session?

- _____
- _____
- _____
- _____
- _____
- _____

Now, create your stress-busting playlist by collecting all the songs you've listed.

Play your playlist whenever you feel stressed; it will help alleviate tension and relax you.

Chapter 4
Social Superhero Training

Who's your favorite superhero? Wonder Woman? Spiderman? Superman? Whoever it is, they have special powers that they use to make the world a better place. What if I said you, too, could develop your unique powers for good?

You may not know now, but within you lies a unique ability to use social interactions to improve the world in your own way. In other words, **you have everything you need to become a social superhero**—someone who has mastered the art of connecting with anyone around them.

This chapter is about **teaching you to hone your social skills and take them to the next level.** Whether you are an extrovert, introvert, or a mix of both, it's possible to sharpen and enhance your ability to build rapport, communicate assertively, and cultivate stronger bonds with anyone you want. More importantly, you can learn social skills to stand against negativity.

So, prepare to tune in to your innate social superpowers and begin this journey of transcending into a true social superhero. Step by step, we'll unravel how to overcome shyness, confidently initiate conversations, make new friends, and expand your social group.

Let's get into it.

The Fear of Shyness

You're familiar with that feeling of discomfort and anxiety that arises when you're in a social situation. That deep pit in your tummy when a stranger walks up to you and asks for your name? That's shyness.

Being shy is a core part of who you are; it doesn't just come out of nowhere. To overcome shyness and harness it into a special power, you need to understand where it comes from. There are often various factors at play, including genetics, upbringing, personality traits, and past experiences.

By unraveling the root of your shyness, you can gain insight into why you have it. Don't think of it as a flaw or limitation. No, think of shyness as an aspect of your personality that developed over time. **Reframing your perception of shyness is key to learning how to use it to your advantage instead of working against it.**

Understanding the Fear Associated with Shyness

Shyness exists alongside fear and anxiety. It originates from a fear of being embarrassed, saying the wrong thing, or getting rejected. That fear is the obstacle between you and your potential as a social being.

It's normal to have a negative perception of shyness. After all, it makes you uncomfortable and uneasy. You don't like how you feel in social situations but can't help feeling that way. You want to stop feeling shy and be more outgoing, but you don't know what to do.

So naturally, being shy seems like a problem. But what if you changed your view? **What if you saw shyness as a special gift rather than something to avoid?**

To become a social superhero, you must stand up against your fear of shyness. When you reframe shyness as a self-imposed limitation, it becomes easier to deconstruct. Understand that this fear isn't permanent; it's an obstacle to overcome, and you can do that with the right techniques and attitude.

Like anxiety, shyness is like a beast you must learn to tame. You don't have to eliminate it; you can learn to coexist in harmony and use its power to your advantage. To do this, you need practical anxiety management strategies and tools for increasing self-confidence.

From cultivating assertiveness to practicing making and keeping new friends, the skills we're about to explore can help you build the self-confidence needed to cope comfortably in social situations.

With gradual exposure to social situations, for instance, you can build resilience and gently tame the mighty beast: shyness.

Embracing Your Unique Super-Social Powers

Once you start to see shyness as a hidden treasure, you begin to experience real magic. Shyness is often accompanied by active listening skills, increased empathy, and an innate ability to bond profoundly and intimately with others. These are personal strengths that can enhance your social interactions and relationships.

Being shy makes you an adept observer, a thoughtful communicator, and an empathic listener. Thus, embracing it can boost your social skills and make you a more relatable and genuine social participant.

Empathy

A heightened sense of empathy is one of the gifts being shy bestows upon you. It means you're remarkably capable of understanding and sharing other people's feelings as though they were yours. That makes picking up on even the most subtle emotional cues possible.

If you embrace the empathetic side of being shy, it can make you a source of comfort and support for everyone around you. The ability to put yourself in someone else's shoes and empathize with them can make your interactions more meaningful and compassionate.

Active Listening

Exceptional listening skills are another upside of shyness. Unlike most people, you don't just pick up on what is said. Instead, you hear beyond words—nonverbal cues, micro-expressions, nuances. You detect subtle clues that others may miss.

This is the sort of gift that, when fully embraced, makes you the kind of person that everyone wants to be friends with. **People see you as someone who not only hears what they're saying but also understands what they aren't sharing.**

Listening to others attentively and without judgment can make people confide in you. Eventually, you will become an irreplaceable part of their social group, if you wish.

Deeper Connections

With your shyness comes an inherent ability to form deep and intimate connections with others. It's as if you have a secret key leading to meaningful relationships.

By embracing this power, you can make people feel valued and understood. You have genuine and authentic interactions rather than superficial ones. This creates a sense of relatability and trustworthiness that pulls others toward you.

It allows you to form deeper connections beyond the surface, resulting in healthier, longer-lasting, and more meaningful relationships.

Observation

Being shy comes with ingrained observation skills. You notice the tiniest details, the intricacies, and the subtleties that others might overlook. You're always aware and discerning.

Embracing your inner super observer makes you the kind of individual who notices even the slightest change in another person's demeanor, their subtle emotional cues, and the silent cries for help, if any. Consequently, you can offer insight and support since you notice things others don't.

Embracing your unique superpower of shyness is recognizing that it can be a strength, not a limitation. It's not about changing who you are but learning to utilize the unique social strengths that lie within you.

By fully embracing your shyness and its accompanying gifts, you become someone who bonds on a deeper level, listens attentively with empathy, and forms authentic, meaningful relationships—as in, a social superhero.

Building and Maintaining Friendships

Society conditions us to prioritize romantic relationships. However, studies have shown that friendships are just as, if not more, important to our emotional and mental well-being. Friends bring you joy and happiness, so it's important to have and keep them.

> Having good friends can significantly impact your mental and physical health. Good friends are an excellent source of stress and anxiety relief. They provide comfort and succor while protecting you from isolation and loneliness.

Close friends don't just appear out of nowhere, though. Like you, many struggle to meet new people and form healthy, intimate connections. But however old you may be, you can still learn to make friends and improve your social circle. And that will inadvertently improve your mental health and well-being.

The internet and social media have shifted our perception of friendship. You can meet new people and make new connections with an online profile. Unfortunately, many online friends can't compare to a close friend in person.

Online friends can't be there for you in an emergency, visit during an illness, or celebrate with you during a happy moment. The most powerful and important connections are those we make face to face, so you must prioritize building and maintaining friendships in the real world.

What should you look for in a friend? You want someone who:
- Is genuinely interested in what goes on in your life, how you feel, and what you have to say.
- Accepts you for who you are.
- Listens to you with empathy and without judgment, and doesn't dictate how you should feel.
- Feels comfortable talking about themselves with you.

Friendship is a two-way street; therefore, a friend is someone you feel comfortable accepting in your life and someone with whom you feel mutually trusting and loyal.

When developing new friendships, focusing on how the person makes you feel is crucial. Don't fixate on how your relationship looks on paper or how others perceive it. Instead, answer the following questions:
- Do I feel good when I spend time with this person?
- Am I myself around them?
- Do I feel safe and secure, or like I'm walking on eggshells around them?
- Is this person supportive? Do they treat me with respect?
- Can I trust this person?

The point is that friendships that make you feel good are good. But any "friend" who criticizes or judges you or brings negativity into your life isn't really a friend.

Tips for Being Friendly and Social

As a shy or introverted person, attempts at making friends can make you feel uneasy. However, these tips can help you overcome your shyness to form quality connections and build healthy relationships.

Tips for Being Friendly and Social.

The key to building a rapport with others is showing genuine interest in them. People can perceive when you're genuinely interested in their thoughts, feelings, experiences, and opinions. It's far easier to make friends by showing interest in them than trying to make them interested in you. So, to connect with someone, be genuinely curious about them.

Pay attention.

When you're interacting with someone, switch off your phone and limit distractions. Most importantly, listen attentively to what they say. By truly listening and paying attention to what they say and how they say it, you can get to know them more quickly. Attentive listening may seem small, but it can make a key difference.

How to Make New Friends

It's easiest to make friends with people you see regularly: those you live close to, go to school with, or work with. The more you cross paths with someone, the higher the chances of a friendship developing. So, start scouting for potential friends in the places you visit frequently.

Common interest is a determining factor in making new friends. We are often drawn to those with similar interests, hobbies, or backgrounds. You're more likely to become friends with someone your age. With that in mind, focus on people who enjoy the same activities as you.

It helps to **be open to new experiences** when trying to meet new people. Not every attempt will be successful, but they'll all provide opportunities for learning and fun.

Here are some ideas for where to find potential friends:

- **Volunteering:** This is a great way to meet new people while helping others. It also allows you to practice and hone your social skills.

- **Club or class:** Join a club or class of people with your interests, such as a book club or sports team. You can look online for classes or clubs in your local area.

- **Lectures, art galleries, music recitals, book readings:** These are community events where you can find people with the same interests as you. Try your local paper or library for events around you.

Making new friends is only one part of the journey. Friendships need time to deepen and become more intimate. Therefore, it's important to nurture the initial connections you form by being a good listener and being the kind of friend you would like to have.

Assertiveness Training

Everyone wishes they could confidently express their feelings and opinions. Whether standing up to a classmate or declining an unwanted invitation, we'd all like to be more assertive. Sadly, assertiveness doesn't come so easily for everyone.

Like many, you may struggle with being assertive because you can't find a balance between appearing too pushy or coming across as weak. Nonetheless, assertiveness is one of the skills you must master to become a social superhero.

Reflect on how you express your thoughts and feelings to become more assertive. Are you aggressive or passive? If you're a passive communicator, you put others' feelings and needs before your own.

In contrast, aggressive communication means you violate others' boundaries and rights. Many people conflate aggressiveness with assertiveness, but there's a major difference. Someone who is assertive doesn't bully, intimidate, or threaten others. Instead, they clearly and politely state their thoughts, feelings, opinions, needs, or desires.

Being assertive can help you state what you need and how you feel without being perceived as rude or aggressive, as well as help you take a stand while treating others with respect.

As someone who is shy or introverted, you may struggle with saying how you feel—particularly if it could cause a disagreement or conflict. But we all have the right to express our true feelings.

Here's how to be assertive:

- Rehearse what you want to say first. Write it down and practice it multiple times to prepare yourself.
- Stand or sit upright when communicating with the other person. Do not fidget to convey confidence and calmness.
- Maintain eye contact.
- State what you want concisely and politely.
- Do not apologize if you are asking for something you need.

Suppose you're getting ready for an uncomfortable conversation. In that case, stand up straight with your shoulders back, raise your head, and make eye contact. That's a confident pose that'll make someone take you seriously.

Positive self-talk can make a significant difference if you want to be assertive in the moment. It can pump you up and instill confidence.

Feeling anxious about practicing assertive communication in a real social situation is normal. Start role-playing with someone you're close to. It could be a parent, spouse, friend, or trusted coworker. Try different conversation styles in different scenarios. The more you practice, the better you'll become.

These may seem daunting, so start with the following exercises to practice assertiveness in low-risk social situations.

Here are some ideas:

- Go to a restaurant for the first time and ask for a window seat. Even if you don't get one, it's an excellent way to practice stating your needs.
- Let your boss know that you can't do a specific task that isn't part of your schedule for the week.
- Speak up if your partner insists on going out but you don't want to. Tell them you'd rather stay at home and binge a series.

As you practice becoming more assertive, learn to always pick your moment for difficult conversations. Staying calm is integral to assertive communication. Hence, you should always pick the best time for your conversations.

Gradual Exposure: Escaping the Comfort Zone

Exposure therapy is used for overcoming anxiety disorders, especially specific phobias. Social anxiety is considered a form of phobia, which makes exposure therapy a great way to overcome it.

Gradual exposure can help to overcome performance anxiety and fear of specific social situations. The best thing about this is that you can incorporate it into your everyday life bit by bit without the help of a therapist.

As someone with shyness or social anxiety, you likely face social interactions with dread. Due to this, you might avoid them altogether. But avoidance isn't an effective long-term strategy, so taking steps toward overcoming your social phobia is best.

How to Use Gradual Exposure for Social Anxiety

Exposure therapy involves facing feared situations in phases until the degree or intensity of anxiety experienced in such situations decreases. Let's look at how it works.

Let's assume your feared social situation is going to parties. Here's how you might gradually expose yourself to it.

- First, rank your level of anxiety about attending different types of parties (school functions, family hangouts, birthday parties, etc.) on a scale of 1–10, 1 being the lowest and 10 the highest. For example:

Stressor	Coping Strategies
1. Going to a large social event with unfamiliar people	10 (very high)
2. Having coffee with two friends	5 (medium)

- Choose a task ranked low, as in, something that makes you feel uncomfortable but you can tolerate. Then, execute the task. For example, you might ask two friends out on a coffee date.

- No matter how anxious you feel during the date, stay for as long as it goes on. Don't run away or try to escape the situation.

- Repeat this task once a week until the degree of anxiety experienced significantly decreases.

- Start exposure with a new, harder task.

When facing a feared social situation, refrain from engaging in safety behaviors. For instance, if you usually fidget with your car keys, try as much as possible not to do that.

Most importantly, know that you can't get rid of all your anxiety at once. It's okay to feel anxious. Keep practicing until you feel naturally comfortable in social situations.

Remember, only move on to the next task in your list once you feel comfortable with the previous one.

Conversation Starter Toolbox

It can be tough to start a conversation, especially with a new person. That's why having conversation starters for different social situations is helpful. Whether spending time with friends you don't see regularly or at a party with a stranger, having good conversation starters beyond boring small talk can be difficult.

Naturally, when talking with someone, you want to make sure the discussion is insightful, interesting, and entertaining, and to do that, you have to say something other than, "Nice weather, huh?"

To help you, I have a list of conversation starters to use when building rapport with someone in any social situation:

- Are you having a good time?
- Was it stressful to come here tonight?
- I love your shoes! Where'd you get them?
- Tell me about yourself.
- Mention one thing that made you smile today.
- Have you done anything exciting lately?
- What's your favorite show right now?
- Do you like podcasts? Which is your favorite?
- What's your favorite social networking site?
- What was your last good read?
- How do you know the host?
- What song would you play right now if you were the DJ?
- Cat or dog person?
- Would you describe yourself as an introvert or an extrovert?
- What's something I'd be surprised to learn about you?
- What's your favorite superpower?
- What's the last concert you bought tickets to?
- What's your favorite book of all time?
- Where would you go on vacation without a budget?
- What's your best Amazon purchase ever?
- Are you a fan of documentaries? Which good ones have you watched lately?
- What do you think about the British royal family?
- Who's your favorite public figure?
- What do you normally do for fun?

Of course, what you start a conversation with depends on the situation. For instance, what you'll say on a first date differs from what you'd say to a stranger at a party. So, be sure to choose a conversation starter that's appropriate for the situation you're in.

Exercise: Friendship-Building Journal

We all want good friends, those that feel like blood. However, progressing from stranger to acquaintance to friend can be tricky. It's a familiar struggle for anyone with shyness or social anxiety.

Adding life challenges, changes, and obstacles into the mix makes it even trickier. **Though you may want friendship building to feel easy and natural, you must accept that life's complexities can make intentionality a vital part of the process.**

So, this friendship-building journal exercise is designed to help you figure out an effective way to make the leap from acquaintance to friend. More importantly, it'll teach you to cultivate friendships so they can grow.

I know how incredibly important friendships are, so here are 10 reflective journal prompts to determine where you are regarding friendship building. Get a journal and use the following prompts to write meaningful entries on friendships:

1. *How important are friends to you?*

2. *How have friends influenced you positively or negatively?*

3. *What do you have in common with your friends?*

4. *Are there differences between you and your friends? If yes, what are they?*

5. *Do you respect the commonalities and differences in your friendships?*

6. *When was the last time you showed a friend kindness? What did you do, and how did they react?*

7. *When was the last time a friend showed you kindness? What did they do, and how did it make you feel?*

8. When did you last build a friend up with words and celebrate them for their unique strengths and talents?

9. When was the last time you laughed with a friend? What was the reason, and how can you make that happen more frequently?

10. How would you react if a friend told you they were in need or vice versa?

Exercise: Social Skills Worksheets

The following are two worksheets with a diverse range of social skills. Regular practice can increase social awareness and self-knowledge.

High- and Low-Energy Social Skills

Social skills involve substantial nonverbal communication, such as gestures, vocal tone, and postures. Paying attention to these cues can be a great way to demonstrate empathy and engagement. An excellent strategy for improving your social skills is to always match your energy with that of the other person or people in a social interaction. For example, if you arrive at a meeting and everyone is discussing a new product excitedly, you should match the level of excitement in the room.

This worksheet will help evaluate the energy you and a conversation partner or group exhibit. So, think of the last time a friend, partner, coworker, or social group had high energy. Perhaps they had just returned from the gym or ended work on a Friday evening.

Describe how the person felt—were they excited, loud, and expressive?

How did you respond—with high or low energy?

Now think about the last time a friend, classmate, coworker, or partner had low energy. Perhaps they failed a test or got bad news from work.

How did you respond? High or low energy?

Reflect on both scenarios and find a pattern in how you reacted. Did you match their energy? If yes, that's a good sign. So, make a habit of matching people's energy in a social situation. After the occasion, analyze the situation and determine what you could have done differently.

Exercise: What Does Friendship Mean to Me?

Use this worksheet to reflect on why friendship is important to you. Not only can it increase feelings of closeness and relatedness, but it can also bring clarity to your social interactions and teach you to keep people's needs in mind.

Answer the following questions:

- *What qualities do I seek in friends?*

- *Why do these qualities matter to me?*

- *What do I enjoy doing with my friends?*

- *How do I feel when I'm with my friends?*

- *What makes me a good friend?*

Use the awareness gained from this exercise to appreciate your friends and form new connections. Also, it can be a great way to recognize when people aren't being true friends to you.

Chapter 5
Superpower Activation: Positive Thinking

When people hear about positive thinking, they think it's about training the mind to see the world through rose-colored glasses and never thinking negatively. However, that's neither realistic nor possible. Contrary to that belief, **positive thinking is about harnessing the power of your mind to view adversity from a different perspective, develop resilience, and reach your full potential.**

This chapter explores how you can unlock the incredible power of positive thinking. It teaches you to unleash a mindset that can empower you to overcome life's challenges. Negativity is rife in the world today, and if you aren't careful, it can weigh you down.

Considering the world we live in, you need positive thinking as a beacon of hope and an anchor to keep you grounded and moving in the direction you want. Thinking positively doesn't mean ignoring challenges or living in a fantasy world. Instead, it means nurturing a positive mindset by proactively seeking solutions to your problems.

> Positive thinking can guide you toward motivation and a brighter outlook on anything that happens to you. It gives you the resilience to face and overcome the most difficult setbacks.

In this chapter, you and I will explore the core of positive thinking. You'll learn about what fuels it, the power of self-belief, and how to start finding opportunities in challenges. You'll even learn about the scientific explanation behind the power of positive thinking.

The Power of Positive Thinking

"Is your glass half-empty or half-full?"

If someone were to ask this, what would be your answer? This is an age-old question, and how you answer it can provide some helpful insight into your mindset, outlook, and worldview.

The power of positive thinking is amazing. Sure, the idea that you can change your life with just your mind may seem like science fiction. But the reality is that having a positive outlook and mindset can make all the difference.

Negative and positive thinking are both powerful, but they create opposite results. Positive thinking doesn't mean ignoring your problems; it simply means taking a productive approach to addressing them. Instead of thinking that the worst will happen, you convince yourself that something good will come from it.

Being a positive thinker means you seek solutions and are confident you'll find them. Rather than complain about difficulties, you find ways to overcome them. You take charge of your life because you know nobody else but you can determine how it goes.

> A positive thinker looks for the bright side of difficulties and is optimistic things will work out. A positive mindset means having an optimistic outlook, which means having hope.

Positive thinking stems from your inner self-talk: the endless stream of thoughts popping in and out of your head. These thoughts are either positive or negative. Some stem from logic and reason, whereas others come from cognitive biases and misconceptions due to preconceived ideas.

Take a moment to examine the thoughts running through your mind. If they're mostly negative, you have a pessimistic outlook on life. In contrast, if they're mostly positive, your outlook on life is optimistic.

Individuals with a pessimistic mindset tend to blame themselves and others when bad things occur but will never give themselves credit when things go their way. They are predisposed to viewing adversity as lasting forever. This is unhealthy because blaming yourself for unfortunate events or things that are out of your control can negatively impact your mental health and well-being.

Conversely, those with an optimistic mindset do not blame themselves for bad outcomes and usually take credit when good things happen. They also view adverse events as temporary and unusual.

Research has linked positive thinking to various health benefits, including:

- Improved stress management and coping mechanisms
- Better mental and emotional health
- Better physical well-being
- Lower depression rates
- Lower pain and distress levels
- Increased resistance to illness
- Reduced risk of heart disease
- Increased life span

A positive outlook equips you to take action, think creatively, cope with stress, and engage in creative problem-solving. It also puts you in a better mood, enabling you to create more positive connections with new acquaintances, friends, family members, and colleagues.

How does positive thinking manifest?

When you have a positive mindset, you live a healthy lifestyle. You smile more, remain calm under pressure, and are pleasant. A person who thinks positively is often willing to explore new things. This leads to improved self-esteem.

The thing about positive thinking is that it's infectious. When you're positively minded, you can't help but share it with those around you.

Negative thinking limits brain activity and your ability to make informed decisions. In the face of intense emotions like fear, it's hard to think about anything other than what you're afraid of. That's how crippling negative thoughts can be.

This can be detrimental as fear prevents you from taking on new adventures that could change your life forever. The same applies to other emotions, such as anger, sadness, guilt, frustration, and jealousy stemming from negative thinking.

Negative thoughts can obstruct your progress, and a negative outlook can block you from true happiness. It impairs your physical and mental health and overall well-being. Being pessimistic only attracts more negativity to your life.

Blaming, complaining, being cynical, and not trusting anyone increases the chances of negative experiences coming your way.

Practicing positive self-talk is the key to harnessing the power of positive thinking. Naturally, you may be consciously unaware of the stream of thoughts running through your head. However, if you tune in to your thought processes, you can gain more control over the self-talk in your mind.

> The more you engage in positive self-talk, the more positive your thoughts become. If your inner dialogue becomes predominantly positive, you become a positive thinker with an optimistic outlook.

Positive thinking evokes positive emotions, leading to positive attitudes and outcomes. Negative thinking, on the other hand, keeps you in the same spot forever.

Transforming Negative Self-Talk

Research suggests that 70% of the average person's self-talk is negative and self-critical. These are the manifestations of our thoughts and beliefs internalized from early childhood. They shape our life experiences when left unchecked.

Negative self-talk breeds a negative attitude and mindset. The good news is that it can be transformed. In other words, you can reframe negative self-talk into positive self-talk to effect productive changes in your life. The question now is, how do you challenge negative self-talk and replace it with positive thinking?

Track Your Thoughts for Self-awareness

The starting point for transforming negative self-talk is becoming aware of your inner dialogue. What goes in your mind? By deliberately tracking your thoughts, you can recognize whether your self-talk is positive or negative and when it changes. Awareness is central to getting rid of negative self-talk.

Get a journal and write down the thoughts you notice throughout the day. What do you think of when your hands are busy? What thoughts do you have when faced with difficult or stressful situations? Where does your mind go when faced with everyday challenges?

By increasing awareness of your inner dialogue, you can find patterns to identify the negative thoughts you have regularly.

Identify Negative Thinking Patterns

Once you know what happens in your head, you can identify negative thinking patterns. Negative self-talk can be separated into different categories. Being aware of these categories makes it easier to identify and challenge the thoughts. When you can name the kinds of negative thoughts inside your head, it reduces their power significantly.

Here are the six most common categories of negative thoughts:

1. **All-or-nothing thinking:** You view things from a black-or-white perspective. They are only ever good or bad. You also believe things are only good if they're 100% good. For example, if you forget one point during a presentation that everyone else thought was pretty good, you conclude it was a failure due to that one mistake.

2. **Personalizing:** You think you're to blame for anything bad, whether to you or others. For example, you notice a classmate is upset and automatically assume you must have pissed them off.

3. **Catastrophic thinking:** You link unrelated events in your mind and expect a situation to become a catastrophe because another event did. For example, you miss an appointment by two minutes and conclude that the rest of your day will be a disaster.

4. **Mind reading:** You assume that everyone doesn't like you or has a negative view of you. For example, you're having a birthday party and assume that no one at your school will show up because they don't think of you as a friend.

5. **Discounting positives:** When something happens, you dismiss all the positive aspects and hyper-fixate on the negatives, no matter how minor. For instance, if your boss gives good feedback with one slight constructive criticism, you ignore the positive feedback and become preoccupied with the criticism.

6. **Fortune telling:** You anticipate that events will go terribly no matter what you do. For example, you have an interview coming up and constantly think of all the ways it could go bad.

Everyone engages in negative thinking sometimes, but some people are more predisposed to it. Once you can identify the negative thinking trap you're most vulnerable to, you can challenge and replace the thoughts.

Challenge Negative Thoughts

After identifying a pattern of negative thinking, the next step is to take your recurring negative thoughts and challenge them individually. To do this, whenever you have that thought, answer the following questions:

- Is this thought helpful to me?
- Is it logical?
- Is there any evidence supporting it?
- Is there any evidence against it?

Your answers will determine how you address the thought. Any thought that isn't logical, helpful, or evidence-based should be replaced with a more positive one immediately. Only hold on to those that are helpful and logical.

Positive affirmations are the tools for counteracting and replacing negative thoughts. You must make a deliberate effort to get rid of unhelpful self-talk. Do this by changing the words you use in your inner dialogue. Reframe negative self-talk by using positive words.

Your subconscious mind can't discern between positive and negative thoughts. Thus, you can reprogram it to eliminate self-limiting thoughts by feeding it positive statements.

Here are some positive affirmations you can start with:

- I am enough.
- I love myself for who I am.
- I am willing to fail to succeed.
- Fear is a mere emotion; it won't hold me back.
- I am resilient and strong.
- I am proud of myself for daring to try.

- I like myself better every day.
- I can do anything I put my mind to.
- I am a winner.
- I am deserving of love and affection.
- I can overcome any challenge I encounter.
- I am a valuable person.

You can also use these to create positive affirmations more suited to your situation.

Cultivating a Growth Mindset

What do you think about successful, intelligent, and skillful people? Do you consider them lucky or strategic? Do you perceive their traits as inborn or a product of hard work and perseverance? Do you believe that some people are naturally gifted and others aren't?

If you think success results from hard work, that's a growth mindset. However, if you think people are either born intelligent or not, that's a fixed mindset.

Psychologist Carol Dweck introduced the concept of a growth vs. fixed mindset. According to Dweck, people with a growth mindset believe intelligence and skill can be developed. They believe that although some people are naturally gifted, success is the product of constantly developing oneself. Conversely, those with a fixed mindset believe that intelligence and skill are things you either have or don't.

Consider the scenario below:

You studied harder than ever for your recent math test. You read your notes front to back and back to front, practiced formulas, and solved many equations. You're confident that the test will return with nothing less than an A grade, and you look forward to that moment excitedly. But when you finally get your result, you find a C as your test score. After all of that hard work?

- How do you feel and react?
- What goes through your mind at that moment?

Your attitude in difficult moments like the above is a good indicator of your mindset. With a growth mindset, you can embrace failure and find ways to improve. For example, getting a C on a test isn't the end of the world. Instead, you see it as a potential for further learning and improvement.

If you have a growth mindset, getting a C might inspire you to work even harder on your next test and look for tools and resources to increase your chances of getting the desired grade. While you may be frustrated, your mindset dictates whether you embrace or avoid the challenge.

Here are the differences between a person with a growth mindset and one with a fixed mindset:

Growth Mindset	Fixed Mindset
Embraces challenges	Runs from challenges
Remains resilient in the face of failure	Gives up when faced with hardship
Believes intelligence and talents can be developed	Believes you're either born with intelligence and talent or not
Seeks opportunities for learning	Believes they know everything they can already
Accepts and welcomes criticism	Ignores and dismisses criticism
Is inspired and motivated by others' successes and accomplishments	Feels threatened by others' successes and accomplishments

Now that you know what a growth mindset is and how it differs from a fixed mindset, let's discuss the steps you can take to cultivate one.

View challenges as opportunities.

Challenges and difficulties are an inevitable part of life. No matter how good things are, life will find a way to throw something difficult your way. Rather than see these challenges as setbacks or obstacles, see them as opportunities for learning and growth. The more difficult something is, the more you can learn and grow from it.

Reflect on your failures daily and learn from them.

Many of us reflect on what we accomplished at the end of each day. While this is generally a good thing, it can be helpful to include a few minutes of reflection on things that didn't go as well as you planned. What lesson can you find in that experience? The objective isn't to dwell on negativity or beat yourself up but to recognize and hold on to the lesson.

Stop seeking external validation and approval.

Constantly seeking others' approval gives you the wrong objective. You start to see being right as your primary goal rather than learning and growth. Know the difference. Examine when you're seeking someone else's approval instead of personal growth. If you gently remind yourself to find validation within, you will become more comfortable with the little failures.

Celebrate others.

When someone around you succeeds, celebrate them. More importantly, be curious about the reason for their success. You can even ask them what steps they took and how they overcame the challenges they faced.

Incorporate the word "yet" into your vocabulary.

This is the simplest step. Anytime you think, "I'm not good at this," add the word "yet." Say, "I'm not good at this *yet.*" Doing this reminds you that just because you haven't done something yet doesn't mean you can't do it.

As you cultivate a growth mindset, make a habit of learning from criticism.

Do not ignore or dismiss it. Instead, look at how you can apply it to change your thoughts and actions and, more importantly, achieve your goals.

Self-esteem refers to what you think about yourself, which, in turn, dictates how you feel about yourself. When you have healthy self-esteem, you feel good about yourself and your life. That equips you to deal with challenges and difficulties better.

When your self-esteem is low, though, you see yourself and your life in a critical and negative light. That makes you less able to face and overcome life's challenges.

Self-esteem isn't rigid; it can shift from day to day. One moment, you feel like nothing can bring you down; the next, you're thinking of everything that has gone wrong. Usually, you can feel the change in self-esteem throughout the day, sometimes within moments.

> Our self-esteem revolves around our opinions of ourselves and what we have accomplished. It's a representation of how much you like or value yourself. The thing about self-esteem is that it influences our inner dialogue. If you view yourself as lacking, you'll likely engage in self-criticism, leading to persistent negative thinking.

Low self-esteem means you lack confidence in your values, abilities, and talents. It may be due to a lack of security or not having a sense of belonging. On the other hand, good self-esteem means you feel positive about your abilities and where you belong in the world.

Self-esteem starts to develop in childhood. Your parents, teachers, siblings, and friends constantly send you messages about yourself. These messages may be positive or negative, but the negative ones often stay with us more.

Maybe it's hard to live up to your parents' expectations or even your own. Adverse life events such as illness, grief, and loss can negatively impact self-esteem. Personality also plays a role. Some people are predisposed to negative thinking, and others set ridiculously high standards for themselves.

> The four components of self-esteem are self-confidence, personal identity, sense of belonging, and belief in your skills, talents, or abilities. Lacking any of these leads to low self-esteem, which can lead to anxiety and depression.

Try the following tips to boost your self-esteem and self-confidence:

Practice self-compassion.

Practicing kindness and self-compassion is key to feeling good about yourself. This involves treating yourself kindly when you fail, make a mistake, or experience a setback. It always helps to treat yourself as you would a close friend in a difficult situation. Self-compassion increases emotional flexibility, allowing you to better cope with difficult emotions. This, in turn, enhances how you feel about yourself.

Take care of yourself.

Feeling good about yourself is hard if you don't care for your body. Self-care is a way to do something positive for your mind and body, and it naturally boosts confidence. Diet, exercise, and sleep are parts of life that require care. Healthy eating and physical exercise can boost confidence and self-esteem, so ensure you regularly nourish your mind and body with what you need to feel good about yourself.

Surround yourself with positive people.

Take a moment to reflect on how the people in your life make you feel. Do they uplift you or bring you down? Are they critical and judgmental, or do they love you for who you are? The people we spend time with influence our thoughts and feelings, so note how you feel around friends and family. If you often feel bad in the company of a particular person, it's best to reduce how much time you spend around them. Surround yourself with people who radiate positivity and confidence. Let their positive attitudes permeate every aspect of your life.

Do things you're good at.

Doing things you're good at increases your chances of success, making your self-confidence and self-esteem soar. It highlights your strengths, making you believe in yourself, and boosts life satisfaction.

We're all afraid of challenges sometimes. But people with healthy self-esteem don't let their fears stop them from taking on new challenges and trying new things.

Set a goal, whether joining a club or sports team or attending a party. Achieving that goal could boost your self-esteem immensely. Remember that wins come in all sizes, so celebrate every victory, no matter how small.

Exercise: Mindset Shift Journal

Journaling is an effective way to shift from a fixed mindset to a growth one. Ten minutes of journaling daily can make a remarkable difference in your mindset and attitude. Remember that it takes time to cultivate a growth mindset, so you'll need regular practice and patience.

Below are journal prompts to help spark a change in your mindset, but remember that they won't do this immediately. Think of them as a way to start a conversation that can put you on the path to personal growth.

Here are the journal prompts:

- ☐ How can I learn from bad experiences?
- ☐ What lies is my inner critic feeding me? How are they holding me back?
- ☐ What would I do if I weren't afraid?
- ☐ What are practical ways to overcome my limiting fears?
- ☐ What change do I need to make?
- ☐ In what ways can I open myself up to this change?
- ☐ How are my feelings obstructing my growth?
- ☐ What matters to me the most in life?
- ☐ What makes me truly happy in life right now?
- ☐ What would it take to do more things that make me happy?
- ☐ What drives me?
- ☐ Which people in my life make me the happiest?
- ☐ Is my physical health affecting my mindset in any way?
- ☐ Do I let other people's standards influence my opinions and actions?
- ☐ What habits may be holding me back?
- ☐ What positive changes can I make on purpose?

Be Positive

Exercise: Daily Practices for Positivity

Below are three exercises you can practice daily to nurture a positive mindset:

1. Cognitive reappraisal

This involves reframing a stressful or difficult situation to view it more positively. A good way to practice cognitive reappraisal is to watch a movie or TV show and analyze difficult situations. Try to find the good in the difficult situation and come up with advice for the character. What would you say to make them feel better about themselves?

Practice this regularly, and after a while, try applying this same strategy in any difficult situation that arises in your life. Find an important lesson that can benefit you. It's easier to do this if you act like your close friend is in the situation and you're trying your best to help them.

2. "Three Good Things" exercise

Research indicates that thinking of and writing down three good things that happened to you or that you're grateful for each day can increase short-term and long-term happiness. My favorite thing about this exercise is that it is easy to complete daily.

Spend 5–10 minutes every evening reflecting on your day until you come up with three positive things that happened. Then write about them in your gratitude journal.

3. "Best Possible Future" exercise

A 2006 study found that visualizing and writing about the best possible future you could have can increase positive emotions. To try this, take 15 minutes to imagine everything that could go right in your future. Think about the things you want and how they would happen. Include as many details as possible in the visualization.

Regular practice of this exercise is an excellent way to train your brain to adopt a more optimistic outlook.

Exercise: Positive Affirmation Builder

Positive affirmations are powerful statements you can recite to improve your mindset and boost your self-esteem. This exercise entails creating your own personalized affirmations.

Let's get started!

What areas of your life do you want to focus on with your affirmations? It could be improving self-confidence, relationships, academic success, or something else.

Write a positive statement that relates to the theme you chose. For example, if you chose to work on your self-confidence, the positive statement might be, "I am capable and can do anything I set my mind to."

Why is this statement important to you, and how can it impact your life positively?

How do you intend to incorporate the positive statement into your daily routine? Will you recite it in the morning? Write it in a journal?

Now, close your eyes and visualize yourself embodying your mentioned qualities. If you're working with confidence, imagine how it feels to be confident.

What are three actionable steps that align with your positive statement? The steps will help manifest positive changes in your life.

Finally, use the exercise to create multiple positive affirmations that resonate with you. Incorporate them into your daily life to encourage positive thinking.

positive affirmations

Exercise: Positivity Journal

A positivity journal is used to record positive thoughts and experiences. With this record, you can cultivate a positive mindset.

What positive experience did you have today? This could be something small, like receiving a compliment.

How did this positive experience make you feel? What thoughts triggered it? Also, explain if it made you happy, changed your mood, or boosted your confidence.

What are you thankful for, and how has it contributed to your well-being?

Now, create an affirmation based on the experience you've described. This could be a statement reinforcing the positivity you encountered.

How can you carry this positivity forward?

Update your positivity journal daily or weekly, focusing on different positive thoughts and experiences each time. Over time, you'll have many positive thoughts and experiences you can refer back to when you need to improve your state of mind.

In the next chapter, we will discuss how you can build emotional resilience, cultivate problem-solving skills, and cope with failure to bounce back from setbacks.

Chapter 6
Bouncing Back from Setbacks

Setbacks are a fact of life. You flop your school project. Someone else gets the promotion you worked so hard for. After finally getting the courage to ask out your crush, they reject you.

When they happen, setbacks feel like the worst thing ever. Failure and rejection can be devastating. They can make you want to give up on your goal or dream because, well, what's the point?

There is a point, though. **Bouncing back from setbacks strengthens you.** Accomplished people will tell you that setbacks are a key to success. The most successful people you know have all failed at one point in their lives—ask them.

Making mistakes and experiencing failure are necessary for learning how to overcome hurdles and stay strong in the face of adversity. More importantly, they help you cultivate vital strategies for coping with rejection and unwanted outcomes. All of this makes you more resilient. And as you learned in the previous chapter, resilience is one of the most valuable traits you can have.

To bounce back from setbacks, you must build an emotional armor of resilience.
But how do you do that?

Building Emotional Armor

Time and time again, we've heard stories of people who hit rock bottom only to make a comeback and accomplish their dreams. Whether it was becoming famous or earning a prestigious title, stories like these are everywhere.

These stories highlight the importance of having certain qualities. But as great as these stories are, reality doesn't always follow the same sequence. Learning, finding yourself at the bottom, learning again, and moving forward is possible.

What if you experience another setback after previously having hit rock bottom? What should you do then?

Sometimes, you put in great effort, hit a snag, and find yourself in the same position you were in before. At that moment, all you can do is take steps to move forward again.

Doing this requires building emotional armor that makes bouncing back easier. If you've recently experienced a setback, disappointment, or loss, you're closer to building that armor than you think.

Everyone encounters roadblocks and hardship sometimes. And we can all bounce back from a difficult situation, no matter how bad the circumstances may seem. This ability is ingrained in us, although to varying degrees. You may wonder how you build resilience (emotional armor) to keep pain and struggle from making you stagnant.

> **Resilience** refers to the ability to withstand, cope with, and bounce back from challenges and, more importantly, learn from them. It means being able to thrive after adversity instead of just surviving.

Being resilient isn't a fixed state. We are more resilient at some points in our lives than others. The good news is that we can practice and strengthen our resilience. This is what I mean by "building emotional armor." It means cultivating and nurturing your natural resilience to make it stronger.

Having this armor can protect you from mental health problems, including chronic stress, anxiety, and depression. If you already struggle with your mental health, building this emotional armor can improve your ability to cope and thrive.

Contrary to what many motivational speakers would have you believe, it isn't always straightforward to "get over" a failure and keep moving forward. But you can develop resilience if you're proactive about building emotional and mental armor. This means you're more likely to remain calm under pressure and bounce back from setbacks.

Here are five tips for building emotional armor:

1. Seek a sense of purpose.
Seeking purpose is the key to finding meaning in life. Rather than be discouraged by your problems or circumstances, with a clear purpose, you'll be driven to learn from the past and keep moving forward.

Your purpose could be supporting your loved ones whenever they need it, volunteering for a social movement, exploring different cultures, or serving your local community. When faced with emotional hardship, having a sense of purpose can make it easier to recover.

2. Make each day meaningful.
Every day, do something that instills a sense of accomplishment. You can set simple, clear goals that make you more hopeful about the future. For example, your goal might be to learn a few words of a new language daily. It's easier to cope with challenges when you have something to look forward to that gives your life purpose.

3. Believe in yourself.

Having confidence in your ability to overcome adversity can go a long way in making you more resilient. Look out for negative thoughts and beliefs and replace them with positive ones using the techniques discussed in this book. Use positive affirmations to further strengthen the belief you have in yourself.

4. Take care of yourself.

Take care of your needs and desires. Process your emotions and address them. Partake in activities you enjoy. Get plenty of sleep and follow a consistent bedtime routine. Eat healthy. Practice the relaxation techniques in this book. Finally, include physical activity in your everyday routine.

5. Approach your problems proactively.

Ignoring your problems won't make them go away. So, instead of doing that, think about what you can do. Problem-solving skills are a core part of resilience building. Although bouncing back from a disappointment, setback, or loss may take time, being proactive will make the process significantly easier.

Now, let's discuss the bounce-back mindset and what it entails.

The Bounce-Back Mindset

Research indicates that emotionally resilient people have a mindset that makes them well-equipped to bounce back from setbacks. I call this the "bounce-back mindset."

Take a minute to recall your most recent experience with failure or setback. Perhaps you were fired from a job or lost out on a promotion. Maybe your romantic partner broke up with you, or you had a massive conflict with your friend.

What went through your mind in the following days and weeks? How did you feel after the situation, and how did you cope with the emotions?

Though it's impossible to have complete control over your thoughts and feelings immediately after a difficult experience, how you handle them and what you do to move forward is determined by your mindset. A bounce-back mindset means you can quickly recover and look forward to the

Nobody is born with this mindset, which means you can learn it. Even if you don't believe you're the kind of person who can bounce back from adversity, you can still benefit from cultivating a bounce-back mindset. **This mindset can improve your stress management skills, boost optimistic thinking, and encourage you to engage in productive activities.**

The good news is that you don't have to wait until you encounter some major challenge to nurture the mindset and enjoy the benefits. If you start employing the strategies I am about to share in your everyday life, they can help prepare you for when bigger challenges arise.

Here are four strategies for cultivating a bounce-back mindset:

1. Practice acceptance.

When encountering a challenging situation, feeling intense emotions, such as disappointment, frustration, anger, sadness, or grief, is normal. You may also experience anxiety or worry about the future. You may also have repetitive, dysfunctional thoughts about the past.

It's normal to have all of these reactions, even though they are uncomfortable. While your instinct may be to avoid, suppress, or eliminate these, doing so may worsen things.

Instead, it's best to practice acceptance through mindfulness. This means grounding yourself in the present moment and tuning in to every thought, emotion, or stimulus without resistance or judgment.

The goal isn't to change your thoughts or feelings about the situation but to increase awareness and acceptance of them without labeling them. You accept what already is and let it pass. Doing this is an excellent way to work through difficult emotions and move forward.

2. Reclaim control.

Having confidence in your ability to overcome adversity can go a long way in making you more resilient. Adversity tends to undermine our confidence in our ability to change our circumstances. It wants us to think that we can't recover or move forward. But a bounce-back mindset reminds us that we can determine our life direction.

Crises of confidence are even more likely, with setbacks that catch you unaware or make you feel out of control. That's why it's important to reclaim personal control over your life.

There's something called a "locus of control," which is the extent to which you believe your actions determine outcomes. Some people have an "external locus of control," meaning they believe their fates are determined by the universe, other people, or unanticipated circumstances. Such people typically feel demotivated, helpless, and hopeless.

The solution to this is to always focus on things you can control. You are capable of influencing the direction of your life. Shift to an "internal locus of control," which is the belief that your effort, attitude, and persistence are enough to create the desired change in your life.

Reclaiming an internal locus of control motivates you to dedicate time and effort toward changing your circumstances because it makes you believe your hard work will pay off. Like magic, this significantly increases your chances of getting the desired results.

3. Adopt an optimistic attitude.

Attitude is key to cultivating a bounce-back mindset. An optimistic attitude is especially effective for promoting positive emotions and protecting yourself from mental (and physical) health problems. So, try to adopt a more optimistic attitude toward setbacks.

Make a habit of viewing setbacks as only affecting the specific area of your life where they occurred rather than a problem permeating every part of your life. Constantly remind yourself that setbacks don't determine who you are.

Next time you're in a difficult situation, take note of the personal strengths needed to make change internally while also reminding yourself that external forces played a part in the setback. Do not internalize the experience or make it a part of your identity.

4. Seek support.

After facing adversity, you may feel daunted by thoughts of the future or alone in your situation. As such, it helps to have a support network to help you get through the tough times. Support from individuals who understand your situation or from those you're closest to can remind you that you aren't alone. It also boosts your hope for the future.

When seeking support from loved ones, be as specific as possible about your needs. You may need words of encouragement, accountability, or a helping hand with tasks. Ask for concrete forms of support.

Emotionally resilient people with a bounce-back mindset use these five steps to overcome their challenges:

- Accept the setback.
- Reframe the setback.
- See setbacks as an opportunity for growth.
- Acknowledge and process feelings about the setback.
- Have optimism about the future.

Note that not even the best strategies will help to avoid emotional pain. Disappointment, sadness, grief, and anger are inevitable, and you must let yourself fully experience and process them.

Coping with Failure and Rejection

Life is about pursuing things we want, and when we do, failure and rejection are always a possibility. Failing or getting rejected feels bad—whether it's not getting into your desired college or your crush declining your invitation to a date.

Failure and rejection can also happen in everyday situations, such as people not laughing at your joke or nobody pairing with you for a class project. Rejection is the opposite of acceptance; however, getting rejected (and you will at times) doesn't mean you aren't liked or valued. It merely means that one time, in a specific situation with a specific person, things didn't go your way.

The average person will go to great lengths to protect themselves from failure and rejection to avoid experiencing painful emotions. Failing or feeling rejected hurts, but you can't avoid them. In fact, you shouldn't—people who become too afraid of failure or rejection typically hold back from pursuing their goals and dreams in life.

If you often think, *I'm a failure or Nobody wants me*, it's reassuring to know that you can take steps to cope with failure and rejection. **Knowing how to deal with both healthily removes some of the fear you feel and strengthens your resilience.**

The more you improve at coping with rejection and failure, the less they will affect you. But how do you learn to cope?

Here are some helpful ideas:

Be honest.

Coping well with failure and rejection starts from being honest about your thoughts and feelings. When you fail at something or get rejected, acknowledge how it feels. Don't dismiss or suppress the pain. It's normal to be hurt in that situation. Acknowledge how intense the pain is. Did the rejection hurt a lot? Or a tiny bit? If you feel the need to cry, do so, because it's a great (and natural) way to release your emotions.

Talking to someone else about the situation and how you feel can also be incredibly helpful. You will be reassured knowing someone else understands how you feel. Plus, telling someone else forces you to name and express your feelings verbally.

Acknowledgment and acceptance are necessary to move beyond the painful emotions you're experiencing.

Be positive.

When dealing with something painful, there's a chance you'll get caught up in the negative emotions. However, doing so will only make you feel like you're experiencing the situation repeatedly. That means it'll keep hurting and become tougher to move on from.

Admit your feelings, but don't get stuck on them. Avoid thinking or talking about it constantly. Negative thoughts may influence your expectations and how you act. You may become stuck in a pessimistic outlook, which will only cause more rejection. Negative thinking demotivates you from trying again.

Keep things in perspective.

Say to yourself, "OK, so I failed this time. Maybe next time, I'll succeed." or "Oh, well. I don't like that I got rejected. But it happens, and I can always try again." Focus on your strengths and what you're good at. Remember all the times you succeeded and got the things you wanted. Think about those who like and support you.

It's important to give yourself credit for trying. Remember that you took a risk, which is a good thing in and of itself. You may have been turned down this time, but other opportunities will arise.

Use the experience to your advantage.

Often, failure and rejection give us a chance to determine if there are things to improve. It's OK to consider whether your goals were unrealistic or you didn't put in enough effort. You may need to study more, practice more interview techniques, or work on your game. Use the situation to improve your chances of succeeding next time.

Failure and rejection give us a harsh reality check sometimes. But they can help nudge us in the right direction when we take the right approach.

Developing Problem-Solving Skills

Resilience is your ability to recover quickly from adversity. Problem-solving skills refer to your ability to approach problems comprehensively, deconstruct them, and develop applicable solutions within an acceptable timeframe.

Problem-solving comprises five steps:
- ☐ Identifying a problem
- ☐ Deconstructing the problem into smaller and more manageable parts
- ☐ Devising potential solutions
- ☐ Evaluating potential solutions and choosing the most fitting one for the problem
- ☐ Tracking the results and coming up with a new solution if necessary

The connection between strong problem-solving skills and resilience is that anyone with the former automatically increases the latter. Why? Because the better you are at assessing and solving problems, the quicker you can overcome and move on from them. Problem-solving allows you to change your circumstances and attain growth quickly.

To become more resilient, you must develop and sharpen your problem-solving skills to better equip yourself to deal with challenges. The following are tips to help you develop problem-solving skills.

☐ Ask questions.
Being curious and inquisitive is the first step in developing problem-solving skills because it pushes you to think critically. By asking questions, you can get to the root of a problem and start coming up with solutions. Also, asking questions allows you to define a problem accurately to address the correct issue.

☐ Collect information.
You may assume that you already have everything you need to solve any problem or challenge that arises in your life. Unfortunately, that's rarely true and leaves you ill-prepared. So, make a habit of gathering information that is pertinent to your situation. Go to external sources for thoughts, opinions, and ideas to lay a strong foundation for problem-solving.

☐ Be flexible.
Flexibility is an essential trait when it comes to problem-solving. Sometimes, you devise a solution, try to apply it, and realize that the problem requires pivoting. This means that even as you evaluate a possible solution or one you're already executing, you may realize it isn't viable. In that case, you need to devise a different option that can effectively address the problem once and for all. That's why flexibility and adaptability are two things you must cultivate to develop problem-solving skills.

☐ Approach the problem positively.

Right now, you may be wired to approach problems with an anxious and negative mindset. That distorts your ability to be open-minded and honest. But when you take a positive approach, you can address the problem optimistically, which increases your chances of finding a potent solution. View any challenge as an opportunity for growth. Believe that it can produce positive outcomes. Doing so will set the tone for the outcome you get.

The bottom line is that when you're equipped with problem-solving skills, you become more resilient, and that makes bouncing back from adversity easier.

Embracing Change to Thrive Amidst Challenges

You probably think about outcomes when you set out to accomplish a goal. You subconsciously set expectations, and you may become obsessed with the expectations you've set.

When things don't work out how you expect, you may feel disappointed or give up. But life doesn't always go as planned. Though setting goals is important, over-fixating on the outcome makes you miss out on opportunities for growth.

> That's why you must learn to embrace change. It's the key to thriving even in the face of challenges. Embracing change allows you to navigate transitions, prioritize yourself, and become more resilient.

In the words of the Greek philosopher Heraclitus, "Change is the only constant in life." Whether you realize it or not, everything around you is constantly changing. Technology evolves daily, and the world with it. Some things are changing in your life that you may not be consciously aware of, like your music taste, the books you read, or your friend group.

Despite this knowledge of change being constant, we find it difficult to embrace. The mere thought of change is terrifying for many people, and that's understandable. You may perceive change as risky, uncertain, or challenging.

Embracing change means acknowledging that you can't control everything. As scary as this thought may be, it can also be liberating. You must embrace change to grow in life. Doing so increases your happiness and life satisfaction.

So, how do you embrace change?

☐ **Accept that change is inevitable.**
I recommend saying "Change is normal, necessary, and inevitable" as an affirmation. Repeat it regularly when you're going through a change. This alone can reassure you during a transition.

☐ **Make a list of changes.**
Do you know that you're constantly experiencing changes? Are you always aware of them happening? Probably not. So, sit down and create a list of every change you've experienced since childhood. The objective is to realize you've been going through changes all your life, long before becoming aware of them. It also helps to name your experiences.

☐ **Have a growth mindset.**
As explained before, embracing change is easier with a growth mindset. It changes your perspective on life. You start viewing mistakes as lessons, challenges as opportunities, and circumstances as ever-changing. Cultivating a growth mindset is key to welcoming and embracing change. When you see life from a growth perspective, you'll realize that change opens up a path to personal development.

☐ **Practice gratitude.**
Fear of change leads to a pessimistic outlook. This could be due to your upbringing or it could be the product of getting overwhelmed by challenges at a specific moment. The solution is gratitude, a simple yet effective way of achieving a positive mindset. An easy way to practice gratitude is to keep a gratitude journal where you write down three to five things you're grateful for each day.

Without change, life would be static, boring, and depressing. Change is a necessary part of life, and embracing it will teach you to cultivate love and appreciation for yourself.

Exercise: Journaling For Resilience Reflection

You can use the power of journaling to reflect on, identify, and strengthen resilience. Resilience reflection is important because it enables you to identify negative thinking patterns, cope with stress and anxiety, and foster a growth mindset.

Journaling is an effective tool for processing emotions and experiences, gaining perspective, and nurturing a more optimistic outlook. Writing about your challenges gives valuable insight into your strengths and weaknesses. You can also recognize thinking and behavioral patterns that may keep you from becoming more resilient.

Journaling can also help you develop resilience by acting as a medium to practice positive self-talk. So, here are 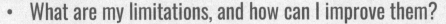 five journal prompts for cultivating resilience:

- What is one challenge I faced in the past and overcame? Which of my strengths did I draw on during that difficult time?
- What are my core values, and how do I use them to navigate difficult situations?
- What are my strengths, and how can they help me to overcome challenges?
- What are my limitations, and how can I improve them?
- What is one thing I can do today to develop resilience?

In the next chapter, we'll discuss how you can build healthy relationships that will positively impact your life and mindset.

Chapter 7
Building Healthy Relationships

Building healthy relationships is vital to improving your mental health and well-being. Whether it's romantic relationships or friendships, it's important to have a community of people you feel connected to—people who love, respect, and support you.

Every relationship has its ups and downs. They all need work and commitment to function in a normal way. But be it a new relationship or an existing one, you can take steps to nurture healthier relationships. Even if you struggle to connect with people or have experienced multiple failed relationships in the past, you can still find fulfillment and lasting happiness.

> All relationships are unique, and people connect for varying reasons. Healthy relationships are defined by a common goal: knowing what you want the relationship to be and in which direction you want it to go. And that's only achievable with effective communication, boundary-setting, and conflict resolution. These are the keys to fostering strong, supportive relationships.

But healthy relationships don't just happen. They are carefully crafted and nurtured with mutual respect, personal boundaries, self-expression, and communication. These are the hallmarks of functional relationships between parents and children, friends, and romantic partners.

What are the foundations of a healthy relationship? Let's find out.

The Foundation of Healthy Relationships

Healthy relationships are characterized by mutual honesty, respect, trust, and open communication. Without these qualities, your relationships will never reach their full potential. In a healthy relationship, both partners put in effort and compromise where necessary. Partners make autonomous decisions, respect each other's autonomy, and share decisions when vital.

Different factors dictate why and how a relationship exists and whether it ends or continues over the long term. The factors that make up who you are, how you see the world, what you expect from life, and how you've learned to relate to others have a major impact on your relationships.

Take a few minutes to think about the relationships you've had. You will remember certain things you didn't like about those people or why the relationships didn't work out. You will also remember something you did like, even if it seems small or trivial. Now, reflect on what you like about other relationships you've seen.

Healthy relationships have specific traits, such as the following:

- The other person respects your feelings and wishes, and you're both willing to negotiate or compromise when conflict arises.

- You feel comfortable talking about your feelings and opinions.

- You feel physically and emotionally secure, and your partner doesn't force you to do things that make you uncomfortable.

- You can participate in your favorite activities with or without your partner.

- Your partner respects your privacy and personal space.

All of these traits are predicated on the founding blocks of healthy relationships, which are:

☐ Communication:
You both feel comfortable sharing your feelings, even when you disagree, and you both feel safe, heard, and not judged.

☐ Boundaries:
You meet each other's needs in ways that make both parties feel comfortable and safe.

☐ Trust:
This means taking their word and vice versa. It entails being open and honest with each other, even if it feels uncomfortable. You both know you can rely on each other and be vulnerable without fear of judgment.

☐ Respect:
You regard them highly and vice versa. You both have regard for each other's opinions, ideas, and beliefs. What you see in your partner is just as important to you as what you see in yourself. Respect also entails admiring your partner for certain traits they embody or qualities they have.

☐ Affection:

In a healthy relationship, affection is freely given and received. You don't have to show the other person you love or care about them, you just do. And they don't take your affection for granted or turn it away.

☐ Empathy:

You both feel and understand each other's feelings. You can put yourself in the other person's shoes and vice versa.

Issues in these areas could indicate that your relationship is fundamentally flawed. So, how do you resolve that? You begin by improving the communication in your relationship, which means learning effective communication skills.

Effective Communication Skills

Communication is one of the pillars of any healthy relationship, particularly romantic ones. A relationship's success often depends on how well everyone can communicate their needs and meet those of their friend or partner. **Open and honest communication makes resolving conflict easier and strengthens your partnership.**

Without effective communication, there will be constant misunderstandings and conflict, which often leads to the end of the relationship. Not being able to identify and express one's feelings and needs eliminates the possibility of conflict resolution. The more disagreements occur, the more they damage the partnership.

But even when the relationship doesn't end, it remains dysfunctional and unsatisfactory. This can impair the mental health of those in the relationship.

To the average person, communication seems simple enough. We listen and talk—but do we do these things effectively? Not always. When we are not intentional about communication, it's typically ineffective.

Before we delve into how you can develop effective communication skills, let's define what it entails. **For communication to happen, there must be a sender, a receiver, and information to be exchanged.**

Some habits and pitfalls can render communication ineffective, such as:

- Silent treatment
- Verbal insults and demeaning comments
- Yelling
- Not expressing your needs or wants
- Assumptions
- Inactive listening

Communicating is important because no matter how well you know each other, neither can read the other person's mind. Effective communication skills are needed to avoid misunderstandings that may lead to anger, hurt, confusion, or resentment.

The following are helpful tips for incorporating effective communication into your relationships:

☐ Be mindful.

Always ground yourself in the moment (pleasant or otherwise) when evaluating your thoughts, words, and actions toward your partner.

☐ Practice active listening.

Listening is a critical part of effective communication. Being an active and empathic listener is a sure way to get your partner to express themselves openly and honestly. When talking to another person, be present, attentive, and focused. It assures the other person that you're interested in what they say.

Active listening tells the other person their feelings and needs are being heard and allows them to include more details or clarify. During a conversation, do not let anything distract you. Turn off all electronics, or at least turn off notifications to fully retain the information being shared with you.

☐ Be clear and concise.

When expressing a need or complaint, include a suggestion for change or action. For example, "I don't like how you leave the dishes in the sink after dinner. I feel like I do everything around here. I would love it if you could do your dishes to save me time."

☐ Use "I" statements.

"I" statements help you appear assertive, unlike "you" statements, which can be passive-aggressive. The latter sounds accusatory and puts your partner on the defensive because they feel you're attacking them when you express your feelings and needs. Using "I" statements conveys how you feel and what you think in a non-offensive manner, ensuring that the other person listens and understands.

☐ Validate feelings.

Validating people's feelings shows them that you understand how they feel. It contributes to transparency and honesty in a relationship. More importantly, it prevents the other person from feeling unheard or shutting down. Always focus on validating feelings instead of addressing behavior.

Effective communication skills are a necessity in healthy relationships. Whether you want to talk about something mild or serious, these tips are great for getting your message across in a way that doesn't antagonize your partner or friend.

> All attachments stem from communication, but **effective communication skills distinguish healthy relationships** from dysfunctional ones.

Conflict Resolution Strategies

Conflict occurs in every relationship. By this, I mean disagreements and arguments. Disagreeing isn't necessarily bad; you can hold different opinions from friends and partners. The most important thing is communicating effectively, particularly in a way that strengthens your understanding of each other and improves your relationship.

While conflict is unavoidable, it can illuminate parts of a relationship that need work. Therefore, it helps to have conflict resolution strategies for managing disagreements and ensuring they don't escalate.

Here are some beneficial resolution tips for managing conflict in your relationships:

☐ **Express your thoughts and feelings directly.**

Sometimes, we assume it's better to keep grievances to ourselves and bring them up "when the time is right." But this only allows them to pile up and build into resentment. You must directly state your feelings, needs, and concerns in a firm and honest manner.

To do so, start the conversation by acknowledging and validating the other person's feelings. Next, describe precisely what they did and how it made you feel. Finally, ask them if they're willing to agree to make a specific change.

☐ **Don't blame the other person.**

You may be tempted to blame the other person for the conflict, but that'll lead to nothing productive. Apportioning blame will make the other person feel attacked, forcing them to be defensive.

An excellent conflict resolution strategy is to always avoid the blame game. Clearly stating how you feel using "I" statements is better. That's how to get productive results. Learn to honor the other person's feelings without putting them down.

☐ **Focus on one argument at a time.**

It's easy to derail an argument. Often, a disagreement on one topic can spiral to others, and before you realize it, there's a heated argument veering in different directions. The best way to manage conflict is to focus on one problem at a time instead of losing the conversation in a fog of related but trivial issues.

Don't try to solve multiple problems simultaneously, as that will only stall conflict resolution. Focusing on one thing at a time can help you reach a mutual solution. It's best to solve one problem first and then move on to the next. Create a list of issues you want to address one by one.

☐ **Practice effective communication.**

I may sound like a broken record, but the importance of effective communication in healthy relationships cannot be overstated. Concentrating fully, listening actively, maintaining eye contact, and responding appropriately will be incredibly helpful when resolving a conflict.

☐ Be open-minded.

Remaining open-minded during conflict resolution increases one's odds of reaching a peaceful solution. Getting stuck on one's side of the argument is far too easy, obstructing flexibility and empathy.

Set your ego aside and strive for objectivity. Consider both your and your partner's sides without bias. Doing so creates an opportunity for a reasonable conversation and the possibility of understanding and accepting your partner's perspective.

Being open-minded and objective equips you to handle any challenges life throws at your relationship.

Boundaries and Respect

Having healthy personal boundaries can help you avoid dysfunctional connections, strengthen relationships, and improve overall well-being with friends, family, romantic partners, or coworkers.

What do you imagine when you hear the word "boundaries"? You probably think of a massive wall that separates you from others. That's true, in a sense. But that doesn't necessarily make boundaries a bad thing. Boundaries are a crucial ingredient in healthy interpersonal relationships.

Boundaries help to maintain your identity, physical health, and mental well-being. They can be physical, psychological, financial, etc. Setting boundaries encourages autonomy, sets reasonable expectations within interactions, promotes physical and mental security, and instills a sense of self-empowerment and respect.

Relationships tend to become dysfunctional and unsatisfying in the absence of healthy boundaries. For instance, if a friend constantly asks you for money, you might feel exploited. Or if your parents keep invading your personal space, you might grow resentful.

Similarly, violating someone else's boundaries might make them uncomfortable and damage your relationship.

Boundaries are necessary in all kinds of relationships, not just personal ones. You need them in the workplace, where there might be colleagues or supervisors who have no regard for your time or needs. Plus, poor boundaries in the workplace can follow you home and destabilize your personal life.

Setting and maintaining boundaries can positively impact your life, from family relations to dating and work. Examples of boundaries to set in your relationships include:

- The right to maintain your sense of self, beliefs, and passions.
- Alone time without interruptions or distractions.
- Being able to change your preferences at any time.
- Agency and ownership over your material and financial assets.
- Being able to take personal time for self-care.
- Having and maintaining your identity.
- Leaving a conversation when another person is being disrespectful.
- Expressing your concerns instead of building resentment.
- Expecting respectful and mature communication during disagreements.

Everyone has a unique way of setting boundaries. Though figuring out the best way to set and enforce boundaries in your relationships may take some time, you must never give up.

If you aren't sure how to establish healthy boundaries, here are some tips to help you get started.

☐ Figure out what boundaries you want to set.

Whether in a romantic or platonic relationship, you can't get people to meet your needs unless you know what they are. Reflecting on your beliefs and values is a good way to determine the boundaries you should set in your relationships.

Answer the following questions:

- What traits do I admire in other relationships?
- What qualities do I like to see in others?
- What behaviors do I dislike?
- How do I enjoy spending my time?
- What matters most to me and why?
- What gives me a sense of fulfillment?

The answers to the above questions can help you better understand yourself and determine your needs. For example, if independence matters to you, set financial boundaries with a romantic partner, friend, or parent.

☐ Evaluate how you feel about the other person.

Reflecting on how others make you feel is a great way to identify the specific boundaries needed in different relationships. After an interaction, think about how the other person makes you feel by answering these questions:

- Did the person make comments or jokes that felt disrespectful?
- Did they make you feel physically distressed or unsafe by raising their voice?
- Do you feel pressured to do things that don't align with your values?
- Do you feel overwhelmed by their expectations or requests?

Reflection can help decide whether a relationship needs boundaries and the type it needs.

☐ State your needs to the other person clearly.

You must effectively communicate your boundaries if you want others to understand and respect them. Poor wording, vague requests, and rushed conversations make this less likely.

Always consider timing. It's best to discuss boundaries when you and the other person can focus on the conversation. Ensure you're both relaxed and calm before bringing it up. Also, mind your delivery. This is where "I" statements come into play once again.

The most important thing is to state what you want clearly. Vague requests are unlikely to get your message across. Be as clear as possible to avoid confusing the other person.

☐ Establish consequences to enforce boundaries.

People will attempt to violate your boundaries if they think they can get away with it. When this happens, restate your needs firmly and clearly. Then, set clear and reasonable consequences for another boundary violation. For example, you could tell someone with a habit of speaking over you that you'll end the conversation the next time it happens.

More importantly, don't discuss consequences unless you're willing and ready to follow through on them.

Learning to set and enforce boundaries can help you foster healthy connections based on mutual respect. Effective boundaries will empower you and lead to healthier, more satisfying personal and professional relationships.

Nurturing Empathy and Understanding

> Empathy is a natural precursor to trust, intimacy, belonging, and understanding. It allows us to understand and relate to one another. It's also why we find ignoring other people's suffering hard.

Nurturing empathy strengthens relationships and improves physical and mental health. Thus, embodying empathy's vital components can help you better understand the people in your life, improving the quality of your social interactions and relationships.

To nurture empathy and understanding:

☐ Prioritize listening to others.

Connecting with and sharing someone else's feelings starts with recognizing that feeling, and that's only possible if you listen and pay attention. This isn't always easy, but it is crucial. If a close friend were to call you and vent about their day, the emotion conveyed through their voice would get your attention pretty quickly. This is harder when a conversation happens with less obvious emotions or amidst distractions.

Empathy begins when you intentionally listen for unexpressed emotions during an interaction. Make the extra effort to notice any signals another person is giving that can tell you more about their emotional state.

☐ Share others' feelings.

Empathy puts you in someone else's shoes when you recognize an emotion in them. It isn't about what you would feel in that situation; **it's about mirroring the other person's emotions.** When you share someone else's feelings, it's easier to address them from a place of understanding.

☐ Be vulnerable.

Empathy is a two-way street. Sharing other people's feelings and being vulnerable can strengthen your relationships. Sharing your experience of challenging emotions allows others to empathize with you, which enhances your empathy by deepening your commitment to empathizing with others.

☐ Take action.

It's not enough to understand what someone else is feeling; **you have to do whatever you can to alleviate their distress or pain.** Knowing what another person is experiencing helps you better identify their immediate and long-term needs. You're in an empowered place to help, and you should.

To improve and enhance empathy daily, do the following:

- Talk to more people. Make a habit of engaging in conversations with those you meet daily. During the interactions, pay close attention to any emotion they are or aren't expressing but subtly convey through nonverbal cues.

- Pay special attention to shifts in energy, no matter how subtle.

- Remain attentive and emotionally attuned throughout the conversation.

Empathy allows you to understand others and motivates you to make a difference in their lives, strengthening your connection.

Building a Supportive Social Network

Having a network of supportive people can decrease stress and anxiety and improve our sense of well-being. Building a supportive social network can make a remarkable difference in your physical and mental health.

The following are essential skills for building a community of people who are truly supportive of you.

☐ Meet new people.

It'll take work, but building a healthy social network of supportive friends can help you manage stress and adversity better. The more people in your life, the more likely you are to build genuinely supportive relationships. It helps to regularly meet new people and add them to your social circle.

☐ Make the time.

Setting aside time to expand and maintain your social circle will be challenging, so you must be intentional about it. No matter how busy you are, always make time for socializing. Manage your time effectively to create opportunities for making new friends and checking in with old ones. That can strengthen your connections.

☐ Listen.

If you've had a tough day, sometimes venting to a close friend is all you need to feel better. Feeling heard and understood can profoundly impact your emotional state. This applies to the people in your life, too. They need that support from you.

Be the kind of friend who is available to listen when friends have something to get off their minds. If they don't come to you first, ask friends how they feel and listen attentively.

Don't try to relate every conversation to your personal experiences. Focus on your friend and their feelings. Listen without thinking about what to say after the other person is done speaking.

☐ Let go.

Not everyone is a good fit for your social network. If you don't connect well with someone, moving on from the relationship instead of trying to force it to work is OK. When necessary, let certain relationships fade away or put them on the back burner.

Again, it's great to have a lot of people to count on for support when the need arises, so be deliberate about building your own social support network.

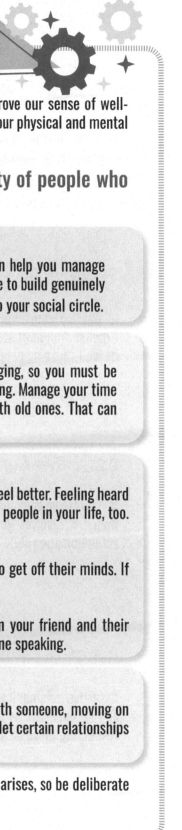

Exercise: Assertive Communication Skills Worksheet

Assertive communication skills are fundamental for healthy relationships. This worksheet provides an overview of the **three communication styles** and how you can recognize yours. It also provides steps for adopting an assertive communication style.

Passive Communication

In passive communication, you prioritize another person's feelings, wants, and needs at your own expense. You don't state your own needs or stand up for yourself. This can lead to being exploited, even by well-meaning people unaware of your needs and wants.

Aggressive Communication

In aggressive communication, you impose your feelings, wants, and needs and bully others into ignoring theirs. It involves getting easily frustrated and being unwilling to compromise. A person with this communication style frequently talks over others and doesn't listen.

Assertive Communication

Assertive communication prioritizes everyone's needs and feelings. It is characterized by confidence and an openness to compromise. It allows you to stand up for your feelings, wants, and needs while respecting those of the other person.

Example:

Scenario	A friend asks to borrow money. This will cause great inconvenience for you.
Passive	"Uhm, yeah, I guess that's okay. Do you also need me to lend you anything else? Maybe my car?"
Aggressive	"No way! I am too broke right now to even borrow money. What else are you going to ask for, my life?"
Assertive	"I don't have a lot of cash right now, but I can lend half of the amount you need."

Your turn!

Scenario	
Passive	
Aggressive	
Assertive	

Exercise: Setting Boundaries Worksheet

This exercise helps define your boundaries. It involves visualizing your boundaries to determine where to draw lines between yourself and others.

Tools:

Get a notebook or a couple of sheets of paper and a pen. **Use A3 paper or bigger.**

Step 1:

Start by reflecting on your current circumstances. Write down the answers to the following questions:

- What is causing me stress or anxiety right now?
- What do I dread each day?
- What do I look forward to?
- Who or what gives me energy?
- Who or what drains me of energy?
- Who makes me feel safe, heard, and valued?
- Who makes me feel unsafe, unheard, and devalued?

Step 2:

Draw a big circle on your notebook or piece of paper. Write down things that make you feel safe and comfortable within the circle. This could be:

- Walks to the park.
- Hugs from loved ones.
- Petting your cat or dog.
- Having a structured routine.
- Personal autonomy.
- Support from loved ones.
- Time to pursue your interests and hobbies.

Step 3:

Outside the circle, write down the things that make you feel stressed and uncomfortable. This includes anything that tests your limits, like:

- Friends asking to borrow money or personal items.
- Your roommate touching your stuff without consent.
- Working late.
- Coworkers gossiping.
- Your partner invading the privacy of your mobile device.
- Your sibling only calling when they need your help.
- Your parent telling you how to live your life.
- Worrying about people's opinions of you.

At the end of this exercise, you should know the areas of your life that need boundaries and the type of boundaries needed.

The final chapter explores how you can embrace your unique strengths, set SMART goals, and begin a lifelong journey toward a resilient and supercharged life.

Chapter 8
Super Teen, Super Life

Welcome to the final chapter, where we'll explore how you can become a "super teen" with a "super life." This chapter is your guide to unlocking the extraordinary potential within you, helping you navigate the challenges of adolescence with confidence and resilience.

Just like a superhero discovers their special abilities, you possess unique qualities that make you exceptional. We'll delve into the art of recognizing and embracing these superpowers and understanding that they are the key to unlocking your full potential.

Fear of the future can be a formidable adversary, but fear not! This chapter will equip you with the tools to face the unknown with courage and determination. By embracing a mindset of continuous learning and resilience, you'll transform uncertainty into an adventure of self-discovery.

Setting goals is your superpower for shaping a bright and purposeful future. We'll walk through practical steps to define your aspirations, break them into achievable tasks, and prioritize them based on your values.

> ## Your goals are the compass guiding you toward the life you envision.

Let's start by looking at how you can embrace your superpowers.

Embracing Your Unique Superpowers

Life can be a rollercoaster, and being a teen comes with its own set of challenges and triumphs. But here's the inside scoop: **You've got some seriously cool superpowers waiting to be unleashed. Yes, you heard it right—superpowers.** Not the kind you see in comic books, but unique abilities that make you, well, YOU. Let's dive into how you can embrace these superpowers and make the most of your teenage years.

The Power of Individuality

First, let's talk about the power of individuality. You're like a snowflake; no two are alike. Your quirks, your interests, and your perspective on the world make you one of a kind. Instead of trying to fit into a mold, embrace what makes you unique. Whether it's a love for obscure hobbies, a talent for drawing, or a fascination with astrophysics, own it! Your individuality is your superpower, and it's what makes you stand out in a crowd.

The Power of Resilience

Life isn't always smooth sailing, and as a teen, you're navigating the tricky waters of adolescence. But guess what? You're tougher than you think. Embrace the bumps and bruises, the failures and setbacks. Each one is a lesson that adds to your superpower of resilience. When things get tough, remember you have the strength to bounce back, learn, and grow. The ability to face challenges head-on is a superpower that will serve you well throughout your life.

The Power of Curiosity

You've probably heard the saying "Curiosity killed the cat," but in your case, curiosity is your secret weapon. The teenage years are a time of exploration and discovery. Don't be afraid to ask questions, seek knowledge, and dive into new experiences. Your curious nature is a superpower that opens doors to endless possibilities. It's the key to expanding your horizons and uncovering hidden talents and passions.

The Power of Connection

Your ability to form genuine connections with others is a superpower in a world that often feels more connected digitally than personally. Your friendships, empathy, and understanding of different perspectives are invaluable.

Embrace the power of human connection, whether it's through a heartfelt conversation, a shared laugh, or a supportive shoulder during tough times. Your ability to connect with others is a superpower that fosters a sense of community and makes the world a better place.

The Power of Adaptability

The world is constantly changing, and your ability to adapt is a superpower that will serve you well in the long run. Embrace change as an opportunity for growth and learning. Whether it's adapting to new technology, navigating shifts in relationships, or facing unexpected challenges, your flexibility is a superpower that keeps you resilient and ready for whatever comes your way.

The Power of Kindness

In a world that can sometimes be harsh, your ability to show kindness is a superpower that can make a significant impact. Whether it's a small act of kindness, a friendly smile, or a supportive gesture, your compassion can brighten someone's day and create a ripple effect of positivity. Embrace your superpower of kindness and watch how it enhances your life and contributes to making the world a better, more compassionate place.

So there you have it—your unique superpowers waiting to be embraced. Individuality, resilience, curiosity, connection, adaptability, and kindness—these are the qualities that make you extraordinary. Embrace them, nurture them, and let them guide you through the exciting journey of being a teenager. Your superpowers are the keys to unlocking your full potential and positively impacting the world around you.

Overcoming the Fear of the Future

Facing the future can be daunting, but conquering anxiety about what lies ahead is possible. Here are some simple steps to help you overcome the fear of the future:

Acknowledge your fears.

It's okay to feel uncertain or anxious about what's to come. Accepting your emotions is the first step towards overcoming them. Take a moment to identify specific concerns and write them down. This simple act of putting your fears on paper can make them seem more manageable.

Focus on the present.

The future may seem overwhelming, but remember, you can shape it through your actions today. Break down your long-term goals into smaller, more achievable steps. By concentrating on what you can do now, you'll build a foundation for a more secure future.

Set realistic expectations.

Understand that life is full of uncertainties; not everything can be predicted or controlled. Embrace the idea that unexpected events will happen, both good and bad. Adjusting your expectations will make you better equipped to adapt to whatever comes your way.

Develop a plan.

Outline your goals and create a roadmap to reach them. Having a plan provides a sense of direction and purpose, which can help alleviate the fear of the unknown. Break your plan into actionable steps and celebrate small victories along the way. This will build confidence and make the journey seem less intimidating.

Cultivate a positive mindset.

Challenge negative thoughts about the future by focusing on the potential for growth and learning. Replace thoughts of failure with thoughts of opportunity. Adopting a positive outlook can change your perspective and help you approach the future optimistically.

Build a support system.

Share your fears with friends, family, or a trusted mentor. Sometimes, voicing your concerns out loud makes them less overwhelming. Surround yourself with people who encourage and support you. Having a reliable support system can provide comfort and guidance during uncertain times.

Practice mindfulness.

Learn to live in the present moment by practicing mindfulness techniques, such as meditation, deep breathing, or simply taking a moment to appreciate your surroundings. Mindfulness can help calm your mind and reduce anxiety about the future.

Educate yourself.

Knowledge is a powerful tool in overcoming fear. Take the time to research and understand the factors that contribute to your anxiety. The more informed you are, the better equipped you'll be to face challenges and make informed decisions.

Remember, you're not alone in feeling apprehensive about the future. Many share your experience. By taking small, proactive steps and adopting a positive mindset, you can gradually overcome your fear and embrace the opportunities that lie ahead.

Be Positive

Goal Setting for a Bright Future

Embarking on setting goals is akin to planting the seeds for a flourishing future. It is a deliberate and empowering process that propels you towards the life you envision. As you navigate the terrain of aspirations and ambitions, the art of goal setting becomes your compass, guiding you through the intricacies of personal growth and achievement.

Here, we'll delve into practical steps, employing a straightforward approach to help you set goals and cultivate a roadmap for a future brimming with purpose and fulfillment.

☐ Reflect on your values and priorities.

Commence this journey by delving into your innermost thoughts. What values resonate deeply with you? Perhaps family, personal development, or community service holds significance. Jot down these core values, as they will serve as the guiding principles for your goals.

For instance, if community service is a priority, a goal might be volunteering at a local organization regularly.

☐ Define your long-term vision.

Picture your ideal future. Envision the person you aim to become and the life you wish to lead in five, 10, or 20 years. This overarching vision acts as a beacon, illuminating your path and giving context to the goals you set. Let's say your vision involves a career in sustainable technology. Your goals could include acquiring relevant skills, attending industry conferences, and securing an internship.

☐ Break down your goals.

Monumental goals can appear overwhelming at first glance. Break them down into smaller, bite-sized tasks to make them more manageable. If your long-term goal is to launch your business, break it down. Start by researching your industry, creating a business plan, and saving a specific amount of money to kickstart your venture. These incremental steps make the process less daunting and allow you to celebrate achievements along the way.

☐ Set SMART goals.

Precision is the key to effective goal setting. Ensure your goals are SMART: Specific, Measurable, Achievable, Relevant, and Time-bound. Let's consider a health-related goal. Instead of a vague resolution like "I want to get fit," transform it into a SMART goal like "I will jog for 30 minutes every morning for the next three months." This goal is specific (jogging), measurable (30 minutes), achievable (considering your current fitness level), relevant (contributing to overall fitness), and time-bound (three months).

☐ Prioritize your goals.

Recognize that not all goals carry equal weight. Prioritize them based on their significance in shaping your long-term vision. Suppose your vision includes a balance between career success and family life. Prioritize goals that contribute to both aspects, such as completing a professional development course and allocating quality time for your family. This strategic approach ensures that your time and energy are invested where they matter most.

☐ Create an action plan with specific examples.

Once you have identified your goals, create an action plan with specific steps. If your goal is career-oriented, the action plan might include updating your resume, networking with professionals in your industry, and applying for relevant positions. Break down each goal into actionable steps and allocate specific timeframes for completing them.

Next, let's discuss how you can thrive as a confident and resilient teen.

Thriving as a Confident, Resilient Teen

Embarking on the path of adolescence is an exciting journey filled with self-discovery, growth, and the unfolding of one's unique identity.

To thrive in this transformative phase, the following essential elements are needed:

Connection and support

To thrive, every teen needs a solid foundation of connection and support. Surround yourself with positive influences—friends who uplift you, family members who listen, and mentors who guide you. Having a reliable support system fosters emotional well-being. For example, if you're navigating challenges at school, having a friend to talk to or seeking guidance from a trusted teacher can make a significant difference.

Healthy relationships

Building healthy relationships is crucial for your well-being. Seek connections based on respect, understanding, and shared values. Whether it's friendships, romantic relationships, or family ties, prioritize those that contribute positively to your life. Healthy relationships provide a sense of belonging and contribute to your overall happiness.

Emotional well-being

Thriving as a teen involves nurturing your emotional well-being. Understand and express your feelings, and don't hesitate to seek professional help if needed. Developing emotional intelligence equips you to navigate the ups and downs of adolescence. For instance, acknowledging your emotions and discussing them with a counselor can be valuable if you're feeling overwhelmed with school pressure.

Educational support

To thrive academically, tap into educational support systems. Seek assistance when needed, whether from teachers, tutors, or classmates. If you're struggling with a particular subject, don't hesitate to ask questions or attend after-school study sessions. Taking proactive steps to enhance your learning experience contributes to your academic success.

Personal independence

Cultivating personal independence is vital to thriving as a teen. Develop decision-making skills and take responsibility for your choices. For instance, effectively managing your time for homework, chores, and personal interests fosters a sense of autonomy. Learning to make informed decisions sets the stage for a confident and independent future.

Healthy habits

Thriving involves taking care of your physical well-being. Adopt healthy habits, including regular exercise, balanced nutrition, and sufficient sleep. If, for example, you enjoy playing a sport, engaging in regular physical activity not only contributes to your physical health but also boosts your mood and overall well-being.

Time management skills

Developing effective time management skills is essential for juggling the demands of adolescence. Prioritize tasks, set realistic deadlines, and allocate time for responsibilities and leisure. For example, if you balance schoolwork and part-time employment, creating a schedule helps maintain a healthy balance between academics and work.

Resilience in the face of challenges

Thriving teens possess resilience—the ability to bounce back from setbacks. Understand that challenges are a natural part of life, and developing resilience equips you to face adversity. If, for instance, you face criticism or setbacks in a personal project, view them as opportunities to learn and grow, adapting your approach with resilience.

Digital literacy and balance

In today's digital age, thriving includes developing digital literacy and maintaining a healthy balance in your online life. Use technology responsibly, be aware of online safety, and balance screen time with offline activities. If you enjoy social media, being mindful of your usage and ensuring it doesn't impact your well-being is crucial.

Hobbies and passion pursuits

Thriving teens explore hobbies and passion pursuits that bring joy and fulfillment. Whether painting, coding, playing a sport, or writing, dedicating time to activities you love contributes to a well-rounded and fulfilling teen experience. Pursuing passions fosters creativity, self-expression, and a sense of accomplishment.

By nurturing these aspects, you build a strong foundation for surviving and flourishing during these formative years.

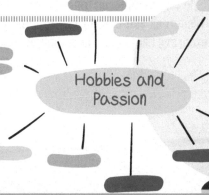

Hobbies and Passion

Exercise: Cultivating a Lifelong Learning Mindset

Embracing a mindset that values continuous learning is like opening a door to endless possibilities. This worksheet is designed to guide you through practical steps to foster such a mindset, which will serve you well throughout your life.

Reflect on your curiosities.

Start by reflecting on topics that genuinely interest you. What subjects or activities spark your curiosity? Write down at least three things you're eager to learn more about. For example, it could be mastering a new language, exploring robotics, or delving into sustainable living.

1
2
3

Set short-term learning goals.

Identify short-term learning goals that align with your interests. These goals should be specific, measurable, and achievable within a reasonable timeframe. Write down three short-term goals related to your chosen interests. For instance, if you're interested in learning a new language, a short-term goal could be mastering basic conversational phrases within a month.

1
2
3

Research learning resources.

Explore various resources available for your chosen topics. This could include books, online courses, videos, or local workshops. List three resources you plan to use to enhance your understanding. If, for example, you're interested in robotics, resources could include an online course, a robotics kit, and a relevant book.

1
2
3

Create a learning schedule.

Establish a realistic learning schedule. Allocate specific time slots for your learning activities. Write down a weekly schedule that includes dedicated learning time. For instance, if you're learning a new instrument, schedule practice sessions for at least 30 minutes thrice a week.

Monday:

_____ (Learning Activity)

_____ (Learning Activity)

Wednesday:

_____ (Learning Activity)

_____ (Learning Activity)

Friday:

_____ (Learning Activity)

_____ (Learning Activity)

Seek feedback and guidance.

Learning is often more enriching with feedback and guidance. Identify someone you trust—a teacher, mentor, or peer—to provide input on your learning journey. For instance, if you're learning to code, seek feedback on your coding projects or ask for guidance on challenging concepts.

Person for feedback:

Embrace challenges as learning opportunities.

Understand that challenges are a natural part of the learning process. When faced with a difficulty, view it as an opportunity to grow. Write down one challenge you've encountered in your learning journey and how you plan to overcome it. For example, if you find a particular math concept challenging, your plan could involve seeking extra help or practicing more.

Challenge:

Plan to overcome:

Document your learning journey.

Keep a learning journal to document your progress and insights. Write down your thoughts, discoveries, and any aha moments. Reflect on how your mindset toward learning evolves over time. If you're learning about sustainable living, document your efforts to incorporate eco-friendly practices and any positive changes you observe.

Journal entry:

Congratulations on taking the initiative to cultivate a lifelong learning mindset!

Remember, this journey is about enjoying the process of discovery and growth. Your commitment to learning today will shape a future filled with endless opportunities.

Exercise: The Teen Superhero's Toolbox

Equipping yourself with these life skills is like building a strong foundation for a successful and fulfilling life. This worksheet is designed to guide you through practical steps to develop essential life skills that will serve you well in your journey.

Goal Setting and Planning

Begin by setting personal goals and creating plans to achieve them. Identify at least three short-term goals and outline the steps you need to take to reach them. For example, if your goal is to improve your grades, steps could include creating a study schedule and seeking help from teachers.

1. Goal:

Steps:

i. _____

ii. _____

iii. _____

2. Goal:

Steps:

i. _____

ii. _____

iii. _____

3. Goal:

Steps:

i. _____

ii. _____

iii. _____

Time Management

Develop effective time management skills by creating a weekly schedule. Allocate time for school, extracurricular activities, personal interests, and relaxation. Use the schedule template below to plan your week.

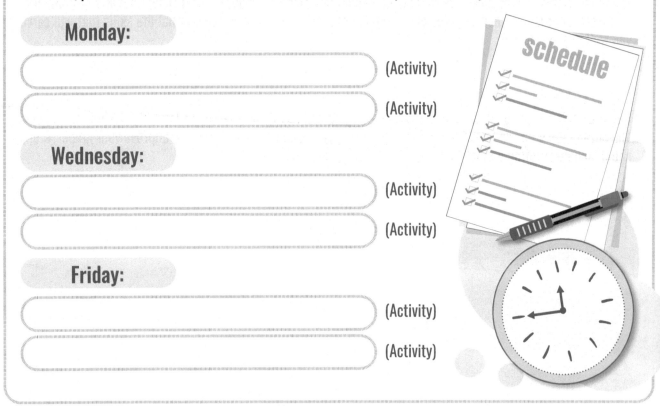

Monday:

	(Activity)
	(Activity)

Wednesday:

	(Activity)
	(Activity)

Friday:

	(Activity)
	(Activity)

Communication Skills

Practice effective communication by engaging in a conversation with someone close to you. Choose a topic of interest and communicate your thoughts. Use the following prompts to guide your conversation.

Topic:

Prompts:

- What do you want to express about this topic?
- How will you ensure your thoughts are communicated clearly?
- Are you actively listening to the other person's perspective?

Problem-Solving

Develop problem-solving skills by identifying a challenge you currently face. Outline the problem and brainstorm possible solutions. Consider the pros and cons of each solution before deciding on the best course of action.

Challenge:

Possible solutions:

- _____
- _____
- _____

Selected solution:

Financial Literacy

Learn about budgeting by creating a simple budget for a hypothetical scenario. Consider income, expenses, and savings. Use the template below to outline your budget.

Income:

Expenses:

- _____
- _____
- _____

Savings:

Self-Care and Well-Being

Prioritize self-care by creating a self-care plan. Identify activities that contribute to your well-being and schedule them regularly. Use the prompts below to guide your self-care plan

Self-care activities:

- _____
- _____
- _____

How often will you engage in self-care?

Teamwork and Collaboration

Practice teamwork by participating in a group project or activity. Reflect on your experience and consider the following questions:

- What role did you play in the team?

- How did you contribute to the team's success?

- What challenges did the team face, and how were they overcome?

Decision-Making

Enhance your decision-making skills by making a decision about a personal matter. Use the following decision-making process:

- Identify the decision to be made.
- Gather information relevant to the decision.
- Consider the pros and cons of each option.
- Make the decision.
- Evaluate the outcome.

Decision to be made:

_____

_____

Digital Literacy

Strengthen your digital literacy by evaluating your online presence. Consider your social media profiles, privacy settings, and the content you share. Use the prompts below to assess and enhance your digital literacy.

Prompts:

- What information do you share online?

- Are your privacy settings secure?

- How can you contribute positively to online communities?

Critical Thinking

Analyze a current news article to develop critical thinking skills. Consider the source, evidence, and different perspectives. Use the prompts below to guide your analysis.

Prompts:

- What is the main point of the article?

- What evidence is provided to support the claims?

- Are there different perspectives on the issue?

Congratulations on taking the initiative to learn essential life skills!

Remember, these skills will empower you throughout your life journey.

Conclusion

Congratulations buddy!

You've embarked on a journey of self-discovery, and I must commend you for that.

So far, we've explored the depths of your emotions, faced the fears holding you back, and harnessed your superpowers. I am confident you gained invaluable knowledge to impact your life greatly.

But before I bid you farewell, I must let you know: Your journey doesn't end here. In fact, it is the beginning, and you must be prepared for what lies ahead. Keep evolving, growing, and becoming the person you're meant to be.

> Embrace your emotions with open arms and don't deny them. Use your emotions as allies that inform, guide, and empower you. By understanding them, you can navigate them better.

Life will throw curveballs at you. Know that you have the strength to handle them; you're stronger than you realize. You've already shown resilience by taking on this journey and staying until the end.

You aren't alone; you have this book as your companion to navigate this journey. Also, talk to trusted adults, share your experience, and be part of a community of young individuals navigating the same journey.

Remember, your teenage years are the foundation upon which you'll build a remarkable future. Don't be shy about embracing the lows, highs, and in-betweens.

This is your story; own it!

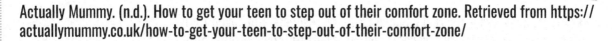

Reference List

Actually Mummy. (n.d.). How to get your teen to step out of their comfort zone. Retrieved from https://actuallymummy.co.uk/how-to-get-your-teen-to-step-out-of-their-comfort-zone/

AFS-USA Help & Learning for Volunteers. (n.d.). Checklist of Twelve Effective Communication Skills. Retrieved from https://myafshelp.afsusa.org/hc/en-us/articles/115002666727-Checklist-of-Twelve-Effective-Communication-Skills

Alexander, L. (2022, July 21). How to Write a SMART Goal [+ Free SMART Goal Template]. HubSpot. Retrieved from https://blog.hubspot.com/marketing/how-to-write-a-smart-goal-template
Alpert, S. (2021, January 28). Anxiety Friend or Foe? Basic Steps Mental Health. Retrieved from https://basicsteps.life/2021/01/anxiety-friend-or-foe/

Ash_Administrator_Ville. (2016, January 14). The Emotional Rollercoaster: Hormonal Changes and Teenage Mood Swings. Asheville Academy. Retrieved from https://ashevilleacademy.com/blog/emotional-rollercoaster-hormonal-changes-teenage-mood-swings

Better Health Channel. (n.d.). Teenagers and communication. Retrieved from https://www.betterhealth.vic.gov.au/health/healthyliving/teenagers-and-communication

Cleveland Clinic. (n.d.). Anxiety Disorders: Types, Causes, Symptoms & Treatments. Retrieved from https://my.clevelandclinic.org/health/diseases/9536-anxiety-disorders

Center for Parent and Teen Communication. (n.d.). Success: Parents and Teens Benefit From Updated Understandings. Retrieved from https://parentandteen.com/defining-success-what-teens-need-to-thrive/

Chea, K. (2021, August 10). 21 Essential Life Skills For Teens To Learn. apis.edu.kh. Retrieved from https://apis.edu.kh/21-essential-life-skills-for-teens-to-learn/

Crevin, M. (2020, July 14). 8 Ways Teens Can Improve Their Communication Skills. Your Teen Magazine. Retrieved from https://yourteenmag.com/family-life/communication/ways-to-improve-communication.

Del Campo, D. S. (2012). Understanding Teens. Las Cruces, NM: New Mexico State University, College of Agricultural, Consumer and Environmental Sciences. Retrieved from https://pubs.nmsu.edu/_f/F122/index.html.

Destinations For Teens. (2022, October 26). 10 Common Causes of Anxiety in Teens. Retrieved from https://www.destinationsforteens.com/destinations-blog/10-common-causes-of-anxiety-in-teens/

Easy Teacher Worksheets. (n.d.). Social Skills Worksheets. Retrieved from https://www.easyteacherworksheets.com/teacherprints/socialskills.html

Ellis, S. G. (2022). Anxiety: Are you my friend, or are you my foe? Sarah Goldberg Ellis, LCSW. Retrieved from https://www.sarahgoldbergellis.com/anxiety-friend-foe/

Focus on the Family Canada. (n.d.). Why your teen needs boundaries. Retrieved from https://www.focusonthefamily.ca/content/why-your-teen-needs-boundaries

Friends Journal. (n.d.). Quaker News - Quaker Magazine Dedicated to Quaker Beliefs. Retrieved from https://www.friendsjournal.org/

Frost, A. (2022, July 18). 166 Conversation Starters For Virtually Any Situation. HubSpot Blog. https://blog.hubspot.com/sales/conversation-starters-for-any-situation

Gateway to Solutions. (n.d.). How to Help Teens with Conflict Resolution. Retrieved from https://www.gatewaytosolutions.org/how-to-help-teens-with-conflict-resolution/

Get The Friends You Want. (n.d.). How To Keep And Maintain Friendships. Retrieved from https://getthefriendsyouwant.com/how-to-keep-and-maintain-friendships/

Ginsburg, K. (2018). Understand How Teens Think to Know How to Talk to Them. Retrieved from https://parentandteen.com/understanding-how-teens-think/

Goodnet. (n.d.). 7 Ways to Nurture Empathy in Your Life. Retrieved from https://www.goodnet.org/articles/6-ways-to-nurture-empathy-in-your-life

Grecucci, A., Pappaianni, E., Siugzdaite, R., Theuninck, A., & Job, R. (2015). Mindful Emotion Regulation: Exploring the Neurocognitive Mechanisms behind Mindfulness. BioMed Research International, 2015, Article ID 670724. https://doi.org/10.1155/2015/670724. Retrieved from https://www.hindawi.com/journals/bmri/2015/670724/

Greator. (n.d.). Fear of the future: How to overcome your fear of the unknown. Retrieved from https://greator.com/en/fear-of-the-future/

HelloBetter. (n.d.). Fear of the Future? How to Overcome It. Retrieved from https://hellobetter.de/en/blog/fear-of-the-future/

John Maxwell. (n.d.). Bounce Back from Your Setback. Retrieved from https://www.johnmaxwell.com/blog/bounce-back-from-your-setback/

Journal Buddies. (n.d.). 54 Journal Ideas and Writing Prompts about Friendship. Retrieved from https://www.journalbuddies.com/journal-prompts-writing-ideas/friendship-day-prompts-for-kids/

Lead Love Legacy. (n.d.). Building Confidence in Teens by Helping Them Embrace Change. Retrieved from https://www.leadlovelegacy.com/blog/build-confidence-through-change

LifeHack. (n.d.). 10 Questions To Help You Find and Boost Your Superpowers. Retrieved from https://www.lifehack.org/301920/10-questions-help-you-find-and-boost-your-superpowers

London Postgraduate Medical and Dental Education. (n.d.). Reflective Writing - The Role of Reflection in Developing Resilience. Retrieved from https://london.hee.nhs.uk/reflective-writing-role-reflection-developing-resilience

Makini School. (n.d.). Nurturing Empathy: Key to Future Generations Moral Character. Retrieved from https://www.makinischool.ac.ke/blog/nurturing-empathy-key-to-future-generations-moral-character

Manson, M. (n.d.). 3 Core Components of a Healthy Relationship. Retrieved from https://markmanson.net/3-core-components-of-a-healthy-relationship

Mayo Clinic Staff. (2022, July 14). Resilience: Build skills to endure hardship. Mayo Clinic. Retrieved from https://www.mayoclinic.org/tests-procedures/resilience-training/in-depth/resilience/art-20046311

McLean Hospital. (2023, March 24). Understanding Anxiety in Children & Teens. Retrieved from https://www.mcleanhospital.org/essential/anxiety-kids-teens

Mental Health UK. (n.d.). Types of anxiety disorders. Retrieved from https://mentalhealth-uk.org/help-and-information/conditions/anxiety-disorders/types/

Microstartups. (n.d.). Networking for Teens: The Ultimate Guide In 6+ Steps. Retrieved from https://microstartups.org/networking-for-teens/&

Miles, C. (2022, May 25). Anxiety: Friend or Foe? UofL Health. Retrieved from https://uoflhealth.org/articles/anxiety-friend-or-foe/

Mindful.org. (n.d.). How to Manage Stress with Mindfulness and Meditation. Retrieved from https://www.mindful.org/how-to-manage-stress-with-mindfulness-and-meditation/

MomJunction. (n.d.). 10 Important Conflict Resolution Skills For Teenagers. Retrieved from https://www.momjunction.com/articles/important-conflict-resolution-skills-for-teenagers_00106119/

Nariman, J. (04 Jan). How to Help Teens Set Effective Goals (Tips & Templates). biglifejournal.com. Retrieved from https://biglifejournal.com/blogs/blog/guide-effective-goal-setting-teens-template-worksheet

Nelson, P.T. (2012). Understanding teens in Families Matter! A Series for Parents of School-Age Youth. Newark, DE: Cooperative Extension, University of Delaware. Retrieved from https://www.udel.edu/academics/colleges/canr/cooperative-extension/fact-sheets/understanding-teens/

Nemours KidsHealth. (n.d.). Rejection and How to Handle It (for Teens). Retrieved from https://kidshealth.org/en/teens/rejection.html

Newman, K. M. (2016, November 9). Five Science-Backed Strategies to Build Resilience. Greater Good Science Center. Retrieved from https://greatergood.berkeley.edu/article/item/five_science_backed_strategies_to_build_resilience

New York State. (n.d.). What Does a Healthy Relationship Look Like? Retrieved from https://www.ny.gov/teen-dating-violence-awareness-and-prevention/what-does-healthy-relationship-look

North Memorial Health. (n.d.). The Power of Positive Thinking: 5 Ways You Can Practice Positivity. Retrieved from https://northmemorial.com/the-power-of-positive-thinking-5-ways-you-can-practice-positivity/

Pangilinan, J. (2022, December 21). 11 Thought Record Examples, Templates, & Worksheets. Happier Human. Retrieved from https://www.happierhuman.com/thought-record/

Paradigm Treatment. (n.d.). Common Causes of Anxiety in Teens and Young Adults. Retrieved from https://paradigmtreatment.com/teen-treatment/anxiety/causes/

Paradigm Treatment. (n.d.). How Teens Can Build and Maintain a Strong Support System. Retrieved from https://paradigmtreatment.com/build-maintain-strong-support-system/

Personal Excellence Foundation. (n.d.). 4 Ways to Help Your Teen Discover Their Superpowers. Retrieved from https://personalexcellence.org/raising-worldchangers-blog/4-ways-to-help-your-teen-discover-their-superpowers

Pikiewicz, K. (2021, December 1). The Power of Self-Awareness for Teens. Digging Deep. Retrieved from https://diggingdeep.org/power-self-awareness-teens/

Positive Psychology. (n.d.). 11 Social Skills Worksheets for Seamless Social Interactions. Retrieved from https://positivepsychology.com/social-skills-worksheets/

Raising Children Network. (n.d.). Teen moods: managing the ups and downs. Retrieved from https://raisingchildren.net.au/pre-teens/mental-health-physical-health/about-mental-health/ups-downs

ReachOut Parents. (n.d.). Problem solving and teenagers. Retrieved from https://parents.au.reachout.com/skills-to-build/connecting-and-communicating/problem-solving-and-teenagers

Reflection.app. (n.d.). Journaling Prompts and Guides for Resilience. Retrieved from https://www.reflection.app/guided-journal-prompts-by-tag/resilience.

Reynolds, N., & Koch, A. (2020, January 24). The Emotional Roller Coaster: How To Help Your Teen Manage Their Highs and Lows. Raising Teens Today. Retrieved from https://raisingteenstoday.com/the-emotional-roller-coaster-how-to-help-your-teen-manage-their-highs-and-lows

River Oaks Psychology. (n.d.). From Stress to Success: 5 Things Every Teenager Needs to Thrive. Retrieved from https://riveroakspsychology.com/from-stress-to-success-5-things-every-teenager-needs-to-thrive/

Sassy Healthy Fit. (n.d.). 50 Journal Prompts to Shift Your Mindset. Retrieved from https://sassyhealthy.fit/blog-1/2020/06/21/50-journal-prompts-to-shift-your-mindset/

Shafir, H., & Fuller, K. (Reviewed by). (2022, December 13). How Does CBT for Anxiety Work? Choosing Therapy. Retrieved from https://www.choosingtherapy.com/cbt-for-anxiety/

Shaikh, S. (2021, September 14). Teenage: An emotional rollercoaster ride. Telangana Today. Retrieved from https://telanganatoday.com/teenage-an-emotional-rollercoaster-ride.

Skoufalos, N. (2016, January 28). Foundations of a Healthy Relationship. GreenTPsychology, LLC. Retrieved from https://www.greentpsychology.com/psychologyofchronicillness/2016/1/28/foundations-of-a-healthy-relationship

Sutton, J. (2021, November 24). What is Emotional Awareness? 6 Worksheets To Develop EI. Positive Psychology. Retrieved from https://positivepsychology.com/emotional-awareness/

Studocu. (n.d.). Reflective Journal 7 - PPD. Retrieved from https://www.studocu.com/en-au/document/the-university-of-adelaide/professional-practices/reflective-journal-7-ppd/15490007.

Swiftfit. (n.d.). 30 Daily Journaling Prompts To Change Your Mindset. Retrieved from https://www.swiftfit.net/blog/journal-prompts-to-shift-your-mindset?format=amp

Tassi Sales and Lettings. (n.d.). 8 Morning Routine Habits To Kick Off Your Day With Positivity. Retrieved from https://www.tassisalesandlettings.co.uk/news/1471/8-Morning-Routine-Habits-To-Kick-Off-Your-Day-With-Positivity

TeenLearner. (n.d.). Growth Mindset for Teens. Retrieved from https://teenlearner.com/growth-mindset-for-teens/

THE BEAUTIFUL LIFE PLAN. (n.d.). 25 Journal Prompts for a Growth Mindset. Retrieved from https://www.thebeautifullifeplan.com/blog/25-journal-prompts-for-a-growth-mindset

The Excellence Team. (n.d.). Resilience Journals for Educators. Retrieved from https://www.theexcellenceteam.net/resilience-journals.

Therapist Aid. (n.d.). Emotions Worksheets. Retrieved from https://www.therapistaid.com/therapy-worksheets/emotions/none?page=2

Therapist Aid. (n.d.). Challenging Anxious Thoughts (Worksheet). Retrieved from https://www.therapistaid.com/therapy-worksheet/challenging-anxious-thoughts

Therapist Aid. (n.d.). Setting Boundaries: Info and Practice (Worksheet). Retrieved from https://www.therapistaid.com/therapy-worksheet/setting-boundaries

The Therapy Centre. (2020, May 23). Challenging Anxious Thoughts. Retrieved from https://thetherapycentre.ca/challenging-anxious-thoughts/

They Are The Future. (n.d.). Your Boundaries Worksheet (Healthy Boundaries for You & Your Child). Retrieved from https://www.theyarethefuture.co.uk/boundaries-circle-worksheet/

Thriveworks. (n.d.). How to Keep and Maintain Strong Friendships. Retrieved from https://thriveworks.com/help-with/relationships/keep-and-maintain-strong-friendships/

Track Football Consortium. (n.d.). Building a Coat of Emotional Armor. Retrieved from https://trackfootballconsortium.com/building-a-coat-of-emotional-armor/

Tribune Online. (n.d.). 5 ways to maintain and sustain friendships. Retrieved from https://tribuneonlineng.com/5-ways-to-maintain-and-sustain-friendships/

Understood.org. (n.d.). 4 ways to help your child build a support network. Retrieved from https://www.understood.org/en/articles/4-ways-to-help-your-child-build-a-support-network&

University of Washington. (n.d.). Communication Skills Checklist. Retrieved from https://depts.washington.edu/edgh/zw/app-zim-supv/web/project-resources/session-2/Communication_Skills_Checklist.pdf.

U.S. Dream Academy. (n.d.). YOUTH DEVELOPMENT: CULTIVATING GROWTH MINDSETS IN TEENS. Retrieved from https://www.usdreamacademy.org/youth-development-cultivating-growth-mindsets-in-teens

Van Horn, H. (2023, April 26). Journaling About Feelings: How to Explore and Express Emotions. Day One App. Retrieved from https://dayoneapp.com/blog/journaling-about-feelings/

ViewPoint Center. (n.d.). The Difference Between Success and Failure: Problem Solving Skills in Teens. Retrieved from https://www.viewpointcenter.com/problem-solving-skills-in-teens/

We Are Teachers Staff. (2023, March 14). 24 Life Skills Every Teen Should Learn. weareteachers.com. Retrieved from https://www.weareteachers.com/life-skills-for-teens/

Wong, D. (2023, April 14). 15 Essential Life Skills for Teens - Does Your Teen Have Them? daniel-wong.com. Retrieved from https://www.daniel-wong.com/2023/04/14/life-skills-for-teens/

Worksheet Place. (n.d.). Social Skills Printables Worksheets. Retrieved from https://www.worksheetplace.com/index.php?function=DisplayCategory

Wright, K. W. (2023, March 9). The Power of a Mood Journal: How Writing Can Help Manage Emotions. Day One App. Retrieved from https://dayoneapp.com/blog/mood-journal/

Youth Empowerment. (n.d.). How To Use Skills To Logically Solve a Problem. Retrieved from https://youthempowerment.com/problem-solving/?amp

Youth Time Magazine. (n.d.). How To Handle The Fear Of Leaving The Comfort Zone? Retrieved from https://youthtimemag.com/how-to-handle-the-fear-of-leaving-the-comfort-zone/

Zen Habits. (n.d.). 25 Killer Actions to Boost Your Self-Confidence. Retrieved from https://zenhabits.net/25-killer-actions-to-boost-your-self-confidence/

Made in United States
Troutdale, OR
03/17/2024